Praise for *The Plant-Based Run*

This book is not just for runners. It's fo
journey, a journey to wellness. It's for anyone contemplating or seeking
a lifestyle change...at any age. It's a real life story of transformation &
inspiring so far! It's a story that proves anyone can change their habits,
set goals & reach them! I will be recommending this book to all my
clients going forward!

@christina.the.healthcoach

The way this book is written, means it's very easy to read light weight
snackable chapters. It doesn't preach or tell you what to do, it's simply
the inspirational story and life of a man who I can relate to. Someone
who went from barely being able to go out for a walk - to being a
marathon and ultra marathon runner. It's an incredible story.

@alexanderhill2020

Whether becoming vegan or not, this book is brilliant, especially if
you're looking to just be better, and being a #fattofit runner, I can relate
to so much of it as well (not the 100k runs like, but maybe one day).

@pinky_pants_

Brilliant book to find the inspiration needed to get my running mojo
back.

@runkuna_matata

The Plant-Based Runner is helping to reinforce my journey of late and
I highly recommend it.

@foreratfifty5

Got this book yesterday, finished it yesterday. Loved it a lot. If you are not a runner or living healthy, you can take away a lot from it. If you are a runner and training every day, you can enjoy the running stories and maybe still learn something new. For me it was so recognizable it made me laugh sometimes.

@running_ron73

Well worth a read if you get a chance and the recipes sound delicious. Thank you Jonathan Cairns, tomorrow is a new day.

@dolbers71

Well where do I begin! So much inspiration, tips, advice. This is by far the BEST running book I have read. I can relate to the author in so many ways. Seriously considering changing our food intake now, such an easy read. Many recommendations on other books to read to help on lifestyle changes for a better you! One thing that I get from this book is that this guy is a regular bloke, down to earth. I would 100 percent recommend this book to any runner out there who wants a bit of inspiration and lifestyle food choices.

@sue1969running

I have literally just finished reading your book & just wanted to say thank you! I've entered my first full marathon for next year & it feels a little bit possible now (if still very scary!) I only switched to being fully vegan last November so learning how to eat well whilst training is new to me too & your book really helped.

@jude_louise_75

FROM
MARATHON

TO
ULTRA

FROM MARATHON

TO
ULTRA

**How someone ordinary gets
to do something extraordinary**

JONATHAN CAIRNS

with Caleb Cairns, Strength & Conditioning Coach
and *The View from the Crew Car* by Fiona Cairns

First edition June 2021

Copyright © Jonathan Cairns, 2021

ISBN: 978-1-9169008-0-6 (paperback)

ISBN: 978-1-9169008-1-3 (ebook)

Book design by George Stevens
Cover design by Alexandra Allden
Exercise illustrations by Maja Todorovic

Important Note:
The information in this book is not intended to be a substitute for the medical advice of a licensed physician. The reader should consult with their doctor in any matters relating to his/her health. Before beginning any new exercise program, it is recommended that you seek medical advice from your personal physician.

www.jcruns.com

For Shay, Jem & Chris

GRATITUDE

There are a lot of people involved in putting a book together. Most have no idea that they may have had a part to play. This is a list of some of them.

To all the readers of my first book, *The Plant-Based Runner*, I take energy from hearing all your stories. Clem Cairns and Ashling Donohoe for critiquing an advanced copy of the manuscript. Caleb Cairns for all the energy spent and advice given on strength and conditioning. We laughed a lot while working on this book. My crew over the years, Jem (my son), Alan Threadgold and Emma Maguire, for being there. Jem, for making the world a far better place just by being in it. Sarah, Dee, Poppy and Deirdre, my daily swimming and coffee gang who listened to me talk about this book for so long. Dylan Macaulay for reminding me that older guys like us don't have to act old. Catherine Curtin, Marie Browne, Gillian Archbold and Ashling Donohoe who have spent many hours running with me over the last few years. Edel Kennedy for her selfless support. Issac Cairns for always being available for nutrition advice. Sarah Lopez for all the walks and laughs. Paul Byrne and Bernard Hyde, my lifelong friends whose company makes me feel like a teenager. Cameron and Kelvin Weymes who remind me every time we run that the glass is always half full. Sharon and Naomi for being my safety net, always there with a smile and a G&T. Simon for reminding me that no matter how hard it is starting out, the gains are worth it. The National Black Marathoners Association for being my running buddies when I started running and was too self-conscious to reach out to anyone who might have known me. Conor Murphy for his support on The Cork and Kerry Trail Runners. Gavin Connors, Orla McGill, Charlotte O'Brien and Helen Finn with whom I worked at St James's Hospital. Their energy and dedication to work, even when there was no recognition or reward, was remarkable. My editors Jennifer Barclay and Ian Smith who made my life so easy. Alexandra Allden and Fiona Cairns for the cover, George Stevens for the book design and Maja Todorovic for the illustrations. Leonie Dawson whose words – *Just write your f...ing book* – I think of often. My sport psychology lecturer Dr Olivia Hurley for her passion. Aisling and Leo Brophy, my niece and nephew, for sending me videos and jokes every time I run an ultra. The Movement Studio for running a business like a supportive family. The Hopsack for being so passionate about everything 'health'. I had to move from Dublin to Cork to get away from Jim and all his staff in Runzone. I couldn't pass the shop without buying a new pair of running shoes. It hasn't worked because his delivery service is so good. My niece Holly Cairns for not knowing how to be anything other than brave. My parents, for always being glad to see me. Grace Dalhoff for making the Düsseldorf Marathon an annual event for me and my most enjoyable. Fiona Cairns for writing *The View from the Crew Car*, and for inspiring, encouraging and working with me through all stages of this book. I feed off Fiona's good humour and enthusiasm every day.

TABLE OF CONTENTS

My Route to 100 Miles

PROLOGUE

If you are full of life, you naturally
choose something difficult and
dangerous. If you have not much life
in you, you only choose comfort.

SADHGURU, INDIAN AUTHOR

Connemara 100, Ireland, 8–9 August 2020

Friday, we set off early for Connemara, County Galway. It's about a three-and-a-half-hour car journey. When we got close, Fiona, my wife, reckoned we should take a detour and drive the last 23 miles of the course, as we hadn't seen it yet.

I got so worried about the hills I almost threw up. They rolled down the coast all the way to Clifden town, where the race finished with three laps, each a mile, of the town. I couldn't think of a more painful way to end a 100-mile race. We continued to our Airbnb but as the evening moved on I could feel myself getting down. I felt way out of my depth. I doubted my training. I had run many hills but I wasn't sure if it was enough to cope with those last 23 miles, let alone the previous 77. *Oh God, what have I let myself in for?*

At 6 a.m. the next day, 49 of us stood on the starting line and ran off into the rising sun. Thirty-seven would make it back to Clifden. I recognised a few runners and I thought of the Vienna Marathon in 2017. I was one of

40,000 on the starting line and the streets were lined with up to 1,000,000 spectators. Today was going to be different. Unlike Vienna I was looking into a long quiet race. There were maybe a dozen spectators to wave us off. I had given my crew a list of instructions the night before, partly humorous but totally true. It read:

1. *The slower I start, the faster I will finish (do not let me take off too fast).*
2. *If I'm thinking of pulling out, tell me to F..k right off and leave me at the side of the road and drive away.*
3. *Make sure I know the difference between pain and injury. If I think I'm injured, give me 30 minutes to an hour. If I look like I have recovered, carry on.*
4. *I am finishing this race come hell or high water. I will get over cuts, blisters and bruises. I will not get over not finishing.*
5. *If it looks absolutely impossible to continue, make me go one more mile before I can even talk about quitting. If I can make that mile, make me go one more, etc.*
   Things to ignore – crying, begging, bribery, diarrhoea, vomiting.
6. *Reasons to pull out – shark attack, death.*

A hot, sunny day without a cloud or breath of wind is unheard of in Connemara. The first few miles were an uphill climb. From mile 10 the sun was rising and the mountain scenery was stunning, better than anything I had ever witnessed, certainly while running. As we got to the top of our first climb we started on our first descent. The joy of downhill, especially the first, can cause a lot of runners to speed up. I could hear shouts from crew members as cars passed, *Slow down, you're going too fast.* With 90 miles to go, probably good advice. Miles 10 to 15 felt wonderful; I could feel the cool of the morning on my skin. Judging by the sky, I knew that wasn't going to last. From around 15 miles the sun was unapologetically out. I had recurring thoughts that I could do well today. Then I reminded myself that I felt that way at the beginning of every race I ever started.

INTRODUCTION

The wonderful paradox of running is that getting started requires no technique. None at all. If you want to become a runner, get onto a trail, into the woods, or on a sidewalk or street and run. Go 50 yards if that's all you can handle. Tomorrow, you can go farther.

SCOTT JUREK, AUTHOR OF *EAT AND RUN: MY UNLIKELY JOURNEY TO ULTRAMARATHON GREATNESS*

This book is for ordinary people, like me. If you are an elite runner or aspire to be one, best look for another book. If you have ever wondered what it would feel like to run 100 miles in one go, then this book may be for you. If you have run at least one marathon and are tempted and unhinged enough to attempt a 100-miler, this book will take you through my process and could get you there.

From the moment I got a bright idea to run my first ultra to now, I think I have changed as a person. I could have been put off by some of my experiences or given up trying. Due to a personality flaw or gene defect I kept going. I have grown with each year of running and this book sets out how I went wrong, where I went right and gives you a path to your first ultra.

When I made the decision to run my first 100-mile race I did one thing to prepare: I ran. Running worked and it got me over the finish line.

But with the knowledge I have now, six ultras later, I realise that I could have done it so much better. From my experiences over each race, I started putting a list together. I added stretching so I could run more fluidly and avoid minor injuries. I added nutrition so I could be physically stronger and go further and positive self-talk to make me mentally stronger. The list now has 20 activities, and only five of them involve running.

There is truth in pain and sometimes a feeling of wanting to make myself 'worthy' of such suffering, but it doesn't have to be that way. I don't think anyone finishes a 100-mile race without some level of suffering. It doesn't have to be all consuming. It doesn't have to be all about overcoming pain. I now know that if you can get an experienced mentor you can avoid many unnecessary pitfalls. This book can be your mentor, your personal guide to your first ultra. Of course there is always choice and feel free to wallow in pain if you are in that place and so choose. If you choose not to, here is your guide. Take it, use it, live it and enjoy the journey.

It takes a special kind of person to choose to run an ultramarathon and focus your thoughts and energy on something that is going to push you mentally and physically to your limits. If you are that kind of person, this 32-week training plan will be challenging and at times painful. Yet the rewards will be immeasurable. I hope this book guides you, motivates you and helps keep you focused. This path you are on will take you somewhere, not necessarily where you expected, but somewhere you will probably never forget.

My Route to 100 Miles

COULD I RUN AN ULTRA?

Don't limit your challenges,
challenge your limits.

JERRY DUNN, AMERICAN ENDURANCE RUNNER

When I look back to my first run at age 46, my dream was to run three continuous miles.

I'm not built like a Kenyan. I'm not even built like a runner. I'm awkward and I shuffle. My gait was once compared to that of a wounded bear. I regularly reached beyond my limit to cross a finish line at 26.2 miles (42.2km) and completed very few of the 12 marathons I ran over the next number of years without feeling like I was about to die.

I run most weeks with a group of friends. Marie, Catherine, Ashling and Gillian. We meet most weekends even when we are not training and usually finish with coffee.

I had no desire in my body to push past a marathon. But one day it happened, just like it has happened to you (or else you wouldn't be reading this).

An ultramarathon is any footrace longer than the traditional marathon length of 26.2 miles. Typically, you will find races are in standard distances:

- ▶ **50 kilometres** (31.07 miles)
- ▶ 80.47 kilometres (**50 miles**)

- ▶ **100 kilometres** (62.14 miles)
- ▶ 160.93 kilometres (**100 miles**)

According to a 2013 journal article, *Exercise Behavior of Ultramarathon Runners: Baseline Findings from the ULTRA Study*, by Martin D. Hoffman and Eswar Krishnan, the average age at which people run their first ultra-marathon is 36 and the average participation age is 43. More than 10% of participants are over 50 years old when they run their first ultra. Clearly this is not a young person's sport compared to other sports. On average, athletes have been running 16 years before they try an ultramarathon.

There's an easy explanation behind the advanced age of ultra-runners: with maturity the emphasis shifts to finishing, as opposed to speed, and as such the pressure of pace is hugely alleviated. Unlike with a marathon, there is no 16-week training plan where you can start from a low level of fitness and mileage and finish the training ready to complete the race. On the contrary, most people require years of 'normal' running for their minds and bodies to become strong enough to endure a distance of up to 100 miles. This obviously favours athletes who have been on the planet, and their feet, for longer.

In the 11 years since my first run, I cannot count the amount of times I have focused on, trained for and burst out of my comfort zone. It's still happening. When things get tough, I remember the movie *Galaxy Quest*, a science fiction comedy, and say to myself, *Never give up, never surrender*. Those early days when I struggled to complete three miles, gasping for breath and jogging with no strength in my legs, have led to this point where I look forward to distance running. Thus, *Never give up, never surrender*, often gives way to, *Who the hell are you?* I don't always know who I am, but every time I break out of a previous comfort zone, I like myself a little better. It feels as if, every time I fall apart, the pieces go back together to make a slightly better version of me.

The 100-mile ultramarathon is an extreme length. It is an extensive physi-ological and psychological strain, placing this event among the toughest tests of strength both for the mind and body yet devised by man. It can be hard for anyone not involved to see what would possess someone to endure such a challenge. Research has shown that most participants approach ultramarathons as a purely personal project. Participation is not without its risks, nor is it without its rewards. Injury is a high possibility and a feeling of immense satisfaction a probability if one completes it. Running a distance of 100 miles in one session takes extraordinary physical fitness, yet no matter how hard you have physically trained, your success might depend on your mental state. The best ultra-runners are often said to be the ones who are most adept at suffering; the ones who, after body and mind begin to fail mid-run, *embrace the darkness*, as ultra-runners are fond of saying. If your mental strength is poor, you will be certain to find out. An ultra forces you to live in the moment.

It began for me with a simple thought. Something like, *Could I run an ultra? Could someone my age, my size, my level of fitness, run further than a marathon?* The thought raced across my brain, a neurotransmitter molecule got a signal from a neuron and sent it through synapses to countless other neurons. Within a nanosecond it was an idea, with legs. One second later and I was already adding, *Could I run a hundred miles?* I knew enough to realise that one cannot just rock up to the start line of a 100-mile race and run 100 miles. So I thought about the marathons I had run and wondered how to get from where I was to where I wanted to be. I thought I should run a 50km and 100km race before I tackled a 100-miler.

I set about finding out if ultra-runners had to suffer, or whether there was a way to circumvent this darkness? *Perhaps*, I thought, *the pain isn't inevitable*.

I started, as I do with most things that interest me, by devouring every book I could find on the topic. But no matter how much I read, nothing satisfied my appetite. Clearly, I needed to run an ultra for myself.

Two years and five months later I would find myself standing on a Belfast street, at the starting line of my first 100-mile event.

If you are looking for books to get going, Christopher McDougall's *Born to Run*, Rich Roll's *Finding Ultra,* Adharanand Finn's *The Rise of the Ultra Runners* & Matt Fitzgerrald's *Iron War* are some of my favourites.

BEYOND 26.2 MILES –
A LEAP OF FAITH

*You're only a success at the moment
you perform a successful act.*

**PHILIP JACKSON,
CHICAGO BULLS COACH 1989-1998**

Ireland is not a place to be a separated father. Any parent will understand the level of suffering you can have inflicted on you by being denied access to your own children. I have been at the mercy of a 'family' court system set up to protect women. I'm sure there was a good reason for this. Unfortunately, the system doesn't always work and the judges I came across were totally out of touch.

As a separated father to three young kids, I planned my working hours around access to them. The time with them, though limited, was precious. I typically worked three 13-hour days each week, and every second Sunday. Working nights and weekends didn't stop me from training. By the start of 2016 I had been running a little over six years and had completed eight marathons. But increasingly, as my kids grew older and acquired their own social lives, more space began to open up. The opportunity arose at work to move from shift work to nine-to-five and, with that small change, I could see how training for longer distances might be possible.

I mentioned to Fiona one day that I was thinking of running an ultra. *Which one are you thinking of doing?* came her reply. She didn't laugh or even give me her *poor man has lost his marbles* look.

I pretended I hadn't been thinking about it for months and said casually, *I'm not sure, maybe the Portumna 50km in June.*

The next day I entered.

I often get asked, *Why would you want to run an ultra?* I find this question difficult to reply to because the answer keeps changing. I'm also rarely in the mood to search within myself for a precise response.

Because the challenge appeals to me is my most common reply. Yet this couldn't be further from the truth. In reality the challenge terrifies me.

We all have our reasons for doing what we do. Some of us are more aware than others of what those reasons are. I may not be 100% sure of my why, but I have a pretty good idea. For me, running is how I cope with the world. I choose the level of pain and I do it voluntarily. It makes me feel like I have some control in my life; the further I can willingly descend into the depths of pain and suffering – as in an ultra – the more chance I think I have of surviving on this earth. This is why I can put my hand on my heart and tell my crew I will not quit.

The second most honest response might be: because my demons are catching up with me and I'm frightened and if I manage to complete the race I know that the subsequent feeling of contentment will make me feel good about myself for a while. It is not a question anyone can answer for anyone other than yourself. Life is tough; if not yet, it will be one day. All you can do is harden yourself and prepare for when your turn comes. Training for an ultra will toughen you up for sure. It's the sort of tough that only you will know about. There will be no flags waving or bands playing. This is personal. The responsibility for your life lies solely with you. If you want to take a step closer to owning it, I'd say that trying to run an ultra is a good place to start.

The process of training for an ultra also appeals to me: the many months of preparation, good diet and exercise. It takes determination, sacrifice and discipline. The outcome is in your hands and your hands alone. I know the sacrifice and effort are not worth it for some, but they are for me. And I appreciate the satisfaction involved in setting a goal, training for it and achieving it; the pride pumping my blood to every cell in my body. As I say, it's a very individual thing. Would I recommend it to anyone else? No. If you don't choose it from deep inside your gut, ultra-running has a knack of chewing you up and spitting you out.

In the middle of June each year there is a 50km and a 100km in Portumna Forest in County Galway in Ireland. I looked at the calendar for the year ahead and mapped my possible direction. I had 21 weeks to play with. Together with my friend and running partner Emma, I had already entered the Düsseldorf Marathon, which took place seven weeks before the ultra. The timing was perfect. I spoke with Emma and she agreed to join me for the ultra. That meant we would train for the 50km race in 21 weeks and treat the marathon as a fast training run. My ducks appeared to be aligning. As it turned out, ducks are not to be trusted.

We arrived in Düsseldorf to find some unseasonably warm spring temperatures, but the gods looked favourably upon us and the temperature dropped from 18°C the day before to 4°C on race day. I couldn't believe our luck. This confirmed a suspicion of mine: the gods are German. It was a great race, too. We managed to stick to our plan and finished in record time. We had trained together for the last year, including two or three times per week in the final three and a half months leading up to the event. The diligence had paid off.

Every Tuesday we alternated between hill sprints and a fartlek run. Fartlek, a Swedish term that means 'speed play', is a form of interval or speed training that can be effective in improving both your running speed and endurance. Fartlek running involves varying your pace throughout your run. Unlike intervals, where you complete a short, fast burst of running followed by a rest or slow walk for recovery, fartlek is continuous running at mixed pace. These were probably my favourite training sessions as we could feel our progress each week.

On Thursdays we completed a straightforward run and Saturdays a long run. We mixed up our long run each week, taking in the Dublin Mountains, the seafront and Dublin's Phoenix Park, the largest enclosed public park in any capital city in Europe.

Seven days after Düsseldorf we were running along the River Dodder, a beautiful route that begins at the base of the Dublin Mountains and unfolds for some 19 miles down to the sea. We joined the river close to my house and ran the eight miles down to Poolbeg Lighthouse at the entrance to Dublin Port. The way back is all uphill and with one mile from the finish, Emma injured her knee. The gods had clearly stayed in Germany, with the ducks.

Training long distances on your own is a lot harder. I didn't fancy what lay ahead without Emma. It's not as if I had a choice, though, and when running, a big part of you is always alone anyway. It is the kind of sport where there is no hiding: every step, every breath, is your own.

MY FIRST ULTRA

A race is a life that is born when
you get up in the morning and dies
when you cross the finish line.

KILIAN JORNET, AUTHOR OF *RUN OR DIE*

50km Portumna Forest Marathon, Ireland, 11 June 2016

The first time I ever heard of an ultramarathon in a way that registered was in one of Scott Jurek's books, *Eat and Run*. I had bought it because I wanted to learn about healthy eating, but I quickly became mesmerised by Jurek's stories of trail and endurance running. It made me wonder what sort of person would find that type of event appealing. I didn't know who these people were. I certainly didn't know anyone undertaking these challenges. Maybe they were just for mountain people. Or people that lived in valleys, like valley people. I was neither, I was a city boy.

I was entering into unknown territory. The night before I slept for one hour only. The course was a 5km loop which meant the crew could set up a tent and create their own feeding and watering stations. The course was 10 laps.

In the seven weeks between the Düsseldorf Marathon and Portumna, I refined my preparations. Not too far from where I live is Tymon Park, with terrain similar to that of the ultra. Accordingly, every Saturday morning I spent three to four hours running 5km loops in, out and around it. When the day came, I felt physically good and somehow terrified at the same time.

The scenery at Portumna is lovely, a mature forest with a brief section beside Lough Derg, a lake on the River Shannon. An open, grassy clearing in the forest housed several gazebos and a larger tent. Each gazebo was commandeered by a runner or a group of runners. The tent was full of bottled water and also functioned as a first aid station. At 7 a.m. on a cold and dry Saturday morning, 127 of us set off. Within minutes we had all disappeared from view into the forest.

It started well and I spent the first four loops looking at the other competitors, trying to blend in. From the fifth lap, the benefits of loops started to become clear. I didn't have to carry anything and I had the option to eat and drink every 5km.

My crew was made up of Fiona, Emma and my daughter, Chris. They fed, watered and encouraged me. When exhaustion comes crashing in, your head can go in many directions, especially when the amount of time on your feet is new to you. On such occasions it really helps to have people in your corner that bring out the best in you. Sometimes the little things become the big things. Fiona hand wrote text messages from friends on a large sheet of paper which she draped over the table at our feeding station. After each lap there was something new, usually rude or funny. On the sixth lap, a smile from Chris so completely filled me that I felt charged with energy for a full 5km. Emma ran with me on laps six and eight. We didn't say much, but then we didn't have to; it was just reassuring having my regular running partner by my side.

Previously, I had always raced marathons. With this being my first ultra, I ran at a steady pace with the target of finishing without injury. I don't remember the run getting extremely hard at any stage. The pain that a beginner associates with ultras never materialised. It was tough but not as mentally challenging as I expected. Still, the relief I experienced when it was over was immense. As always, when you burst your bubble, the pieces don't fit back together in quite the same way. My comfort zone was shattered. I had put my toe in the world of ultra-running and had come out feeling, *I can do this*.

Now I know that a 50km race is like a slow marathon, but I didn't know this beforehand. A barrier was broken that day: when it was over, I knew I could run further than 50km. The fear that had kept me awake the night before was gone. I had been well prepared. I savoured the realisation that I had stepped into the world of ultra-running and had not only survived but felt good.

After the race life carried on, as it tends to. I went back to casual running on weekends. I felt more confident in my ability and frequently drove to new places and ran for hours on end. After months of hard work, it felt great to be able to go out late on a Friday night and not have to worry about a training run the following morning. For six months I took it easy and ran randomly. I got to go to all my kids' hurling and Gaelic football matches on Saturday and Sunday mornings. Saturday afternoons were often spent going out with friends for brunch or coffee. Then, in early January 2017, I started to get ready for the Vienna Marathon in April, which would be part of my training for my next ultra, a 100km race back in the forest.

I searched the internet for a 50-mile race to sandwich in between the 50km and the 100km. The only race I could find was a 50-mile trail run. As I had never done any serious trail running, I opted instead to enter the shorter Wicklow Mountain Challenge. This is a trail half-marathon held each year for a charity, Debra Ireland, which supports families and patients living with a rare but severe genetic skin-blistering condition, epidermolysis bullosa, often known as 'butterfly disease' because the skin of people who suffer from this affliction is as fragile as the wings of a butterfly.

Through my work I had met Emma Fogerty who suffers from EB. Emma is in her early thirties and has never had a day on this planet without pain, yet is chatty and cheerful and positive; I am in awe of her. If you ever feel like moaning about trivial stuff, look up Emma on social media and pull yourself together. It's people like Emma who have, over the years, prompted me to wonder what our physical limits are.

The Wicklow race was fabulous, three climbs and thankfully three downhills, and at one stage you had to wade, thigh-high, through a river. I was exhausted at the end but also revitalised. Not to mention glad it was no longer than a half-marathon.

MY SECOND ULTRA

Once you master breaking down the
mental wall of running, there are no limits.
When you both see and believe that you
can run further, run faster, you can.

ROB STEGER, AUTHOR OF *TRAINING
FOR ULTRA: ULTRA RUNNING STORIES
FROM THE MIDDLE OF THE PACK*

100km Portumna Forest Ultra, Ireland, 10 June 2017

Twelve months after my first foray into the Portumna Forest, I found
myself back at the same starting line. I had gone injury free and was quietly
confident. I had trained hard for this ultra; my longest run had been 30 miles
and I had successfully completed the Vienna Marathon six weeks earlier as
part of my preparation. It always helps to throw a real race into the mix as it
focuses the mind like no training plan can do. You have to deal with issues
of travel, food and clothing and, most crucially, engage in a competitive
atmosphere. I finished Vienna in my second-fastest marathon time to date
and accordingly felt strong and ready for this 100km outing.

I also had the exact same fears as a year earlier. The act of breaking
into the unknown and hurtling out of your comfort zone is at once both
terrifying and exhilarating.

The distance was broken into 20 5km loops, the same loops as the
previous year only twice as many. As I say, I was nervous; it was twice as far

as I had run before and I had no idea how my body was going to react when I hit 70, 80 or 90km. My only tactic was to tell myself that I was strong enough for this. I also had a bad habit of berating myself when I was feeling weak or going through a bad patch. *Get your finger out and stop feeling sorry for yourself, you fat, lazy fool* was quite common self-talk. Three years later I would learn how damaging this can be, and began to take a much friendlier approach. I'm nicer to myself now.

During the race, I mingled with every type of runner. I met a lot of people who were in the same boat as me, which was comforting. Yet at the same time it felt great to be running with experienced ultra-runners. No-one called me an imposter and after a few hours I stopped feeling like one. Finally, after 13 hours and 7 minutes of running, my views on personal limits were permanently changed.

At some point I got talking to a man who told me about an upcoming race in Northern Ireland. It sounded unusual; for starters, it was called *Last One Standing*.

Over the coming weeks I couldn't take my mind off this event.

Around the same time, my mind was opening to new possibilities. I started to browse other ultra-running books in bookshops and realised that this world I had just discovered had a large, vibrant and well-established community. I had been focusing on running marathons. Now I realised there were people running over mountains and covering great distances – 135 miles through California's Death Valley, 106 miles around Mont Blanc in Europe, a six-day race across the Sahara Desert, to name just a few. The list goes on and on; the possibilities for adventure, I learned, were endless.

Before conquering the world, I decided to enter my third ultra, the Last One Standing, later that same summer. I figured it was up, up and away from here.

MY THIRD ULTRA

We are what we repeatedly do. Excellence,
then, is not an act, but a habit.

ARISTOTLE, GREEK PHILOSOPHER

Last One Standing, Northern Ireland, 19 August 2017

By now, I had run marathons, a 50km and a 100km. I had no fear of this
event. In hindsight, I should have been terrified.

Although run in 4.2-mile loops in a forest, similar to the other ultras
I'd run, Last One Standing is a unique race. It starts at 12 noon and if you're
not back from the loop within the hour you are disqualified. Each loop
starts every hour on the hour, and if you're not on the starting line you are
disqualified. There is never a leader and if you want a rest you have to run
faster to get back in time to take one before the next lap starts. There is no
finish line: the winner is, as the name says, the last one standing.

Many times I had run a three mile loop from my house. Running four
miles and taking a rest in between loops didn't seem that hard. I figured I
could do this. I wasn't aware that the pain increased exponentially with each
loop. I thought a few minutes of rest in between each loop would give me
time to recover. I couldn't see the difficulties that everyone was talking about.
I thought this was going to be a fun event.

When I saw the calibre of some of the runners I started to get nervous.
One I noticed had a Marathon des Sables tattoo on his calf. The *Marathon*

des Sables, a six-day ultramarathon across the Sahara Desert, has a reputation for being one of the toughest races on earth. Another runner talked about how he managed to complete a lap of the *Barkley Marathons* earlier in the year. This trail ultramarathon is a hundred miles give or take and is made up of five loops. It started in 1986 and, from its inception up until 2019, only 15 people have completed it. It has a total elevation gain of 60,000 feet. I felt as though I was mingling with giants.

Unfortunately, to start with, I just wasn't feeling it. I felt like I had a slight flu. My legs and my head felt heavy. I put it down to pre-race jitters. When I got back from the first lap I was sweating profusely; my shirt was soaked. I was the same for the next six or seven laps. After that, I didn't notice, but I never got into a flow. Each time I finished a lap I sat under our gazebo and, after the five or 10 minutes when I had to make it back to the starting line, my legs had stiffened up.

I really suffered in this race and, once darkness came, I started to lose my sense of reality. Around mile 45 at roughly 11 p.m., after 11 hours of running, I started hallucinating. When running with a head torch on, if you move your head from right to left all the shadows jump from left to right and vice versa. I started seeing faces and ghost-like figures. On any regular day I don't believe in ghosts but this was not a regular day. I lost track of what was real and for a time I was in a nightmare world.

I think I came out of it when I exited the forest about a mile before the end of the loop. I had never gone to such a place of exhaustion before and I found it difficult to cope. I started to realise that I wasn't up to the task. The race had changed from a purely physical test to both a physical and a mental one. I had really thought I could do well in this race, but I'd had no idea what was in store. The lack of a finish line and the endlessness of running the same loop over and over became too much for me, especially in the darkness of the night. Every cell in my body wanted to stop and I didn't have the mental resilience to overcome it.

I lasted 12 hours, 50.4 miles, before I was disqualified for not making it back in time. I had never willingly put myself through anything like this before. The winner completed 27 laps, 113.4 miles, before being declared the last one standing. It was the most painful and also the hardest event I have ever attempted.

I wasn't dead, so I knew it wasn't the physicality alone that had finished me. I was mentally so far off my game it worried me. It took me a while before I could look objectively on this and learn. I am grateful now that I was foolish enough to enter. Had I any idea of what I was letting myself in for I would have run in the opposite direction, but I now know that it was perfect training for a 100-mile race. I filed it under experience, my most precious file. I made a note to add mental fitness to the chart I had started putting together.

The day after the Last One Standing I got a phone call from a friend to ask if I would be interested in running the Armagh Marathon the following Sunday. I said yes straight away and, seven days after my forest ordeal, I was on the starting line of another endurance fest. Four weeks later I ran the Moscow Marathon. I think at that point I was overdoing it. I passed out after I crossed the finish line.

I was now seven months away from my fourth ultra. Next came the biggest and most savage jump in distance – 100km to 100 miles. I had my sights set on a specific 100-mile race in March 2018 and it was very appealing. It started in Belfast, Northern Ireland and finished 107 miles later in my hometown, Dublin. Why they made it 107 miles I will never know. Every second year they run it in reverse.

There was always going to be a bump in the road and one day I was strength training in the gym and I got carried away with adrenaline. In between bar pull-ups I was jumping up onto a box from a standing position. I left the gym that day with a hernia protruding out beside my stomach. I don't usually let myself think *I'm too old for this*, but the odd time it comes back and bites me in the ass. I carried on running for another year before I realised that I had to do something about it. When I got a chance to take a cancellation appointment in hospital to have it fixed, I didn't hesitate.

After my hernia operation, the surgeon warned me that if I strained myself in any way, it might recur and the next time it could be irreparable. I didn't even go for walks. I hardly moved for four weeks. Then I started short walks for the next two weeks. On the seventh week I went for a run. If I were to skip the 100-mile race I would have to wait two years for the same route. If I left it to the following year, I would be running from Dublin to Belfast and would lose the psychological advantage of running home. For my first race in this category I thought this advantage might make the difference. So even though I had missed seven weeks, I stuck to the plan and resumed training.

The only other 100-mile race that I could find in Ireland was the Connemara 100. Connemara is beautiful, really stunning, and it's coastal. It has two mountain ranges, the Twelve Bens and the Maamturks, and I wasn't ready for that. I had been planning this Belfast 2 Dublin race for more than two years and felt that I had to go for it. I couldn't see a further two years ahead and I had put too much thought into this. So with Fiona and my son Jem as crew, I set off for Belfast.

A SHORT HISTORY OF ULTRA-RUNNING

Why couldn't Pheidippides
have died at 20 miles?

**FRANK SHORTER, OLYMPIC MEDALLIST,
IN 1970, TWO YEARS BEFORE HE WON
THE OLYMPIC MARATHON**

The history of ultra-running may go back as far as the origins of mankind. Early humans were excellent long distance runners, and being able to withstand the fatigue and physical stress meant food for the family.

It was a major step in human evolution, a massive advantage and the most important characteristic of the human body to walk upright on two legs. Freeing up arms and hands meant being able to reach for fruits and carry them for a long distance. Also being upright increased the field of view and decreased the surface area of sunlight exposure which helped with staying cool in the more open habitats of the savannas and woodlands.

No doubt this helped our ancestors become good hunters. Compared to other animals, humans are poor sprinters, but over long distances we excel. We might not have been as strong as a mammoth or as fast as an antelope, but nor were we as susceptible to fatigue and exhaustion. Our ancestors were able to keep their pace and run, getting to their prey with enough energy in reserve to attack in force and secure a meal. Having a nervous system that can produce pain-killing endorphins also helped. Although many mammals sweat, few except horses and humans have evolved to use sweating for effective thermoregulation. This coupled with relative hairlessness would have given human hunters an additional advantage by keeping their bodies cool in the midday heat.

Ultra-running is undoubtedly one of the skills that allowed us to get to where we are now. In the November 2004 issue of the journal *Nature*, a study was published by University of Utah biologist Dennis Bramble and Harvard University anthropologist Daniel Lieberman, assembling evidence that humans evolved and human anatomy looks the way it does because our ancestors were more likely to survive if they could run. The authors believe that running has helped shape human evolution. *We are arguing that the emergence of humans is tied to the evolution of running.* They cite previous research by University of Utah biologist David Carrier, who hypothesised that endurance running evolved in human ancestors so they could pursue prey long before the development of bows, arrows, nets and spears. Another possibility is that early humans and their immediate ancestors ran to scavenge the carcasses of dead animals.

More recently, in 490 BC, Pheidippides, a Greek messenger-soldier, famously ran non-stop about 26 miles from the town of Marathon to Athens. There are debates around the accuracy of this legend, which says that after running from the battlefield in order to deliver the news that the Athenians had, against the odds, defeated the Persian army in the Battle of Marathon, Pheidippides dropped dead. In fact, it is more likely that he ran a much greater distance than 26 miles.

Pheidippides, they say, was employed as a day runner – referred to as a *hemerodrome* in Ancient Greece – by the Athenian military. These couriers were responsible for running for days at a time to give important messages. They trained extensively in order to move swiftly and to arrive with their messages in a timely manner. They were capable of running great distances.

The day of the Battle of Marathon, Pheidippides was probably on duty. However, before the invasion, it had been his responsibility to run 150 miles from Athens to Sparta to ask Sparta for their help, a journey that took about two days. It turned out that the Spartans were in the middle of a religious festival and were unable to leave for several days. So Pheidippides turned around and ran back to Athens to report that they wouldn't be joining the fight, not in time anyway. Although the Persian army far outnumbered the Athenians, the latter proved to have a better strategy and more sophisticated fighting techniques, and thus won the battle. It was now up to our friend Pheidippides to run from Marathon to Athens, another 26 miles, to deliver the glad tidings. And the rest is history.

Ultra-running may have helped us evolve as a species, but sometimes it killed us.

Today, marathon running is a popular sport across the globe. The worldwide growth from 2008 to 2018 was 49%. In 2018 there were 1,298,725 global recorded marathon finishers. But at some point, a certain number of runners always want to challenge themselves more intensely.

There is a record dating back to 1837, when the first London to Brighton 55-mile footrace took place. Then, in 1928, a sports promoter named Charles Pyle envisioned a ground-breaking footrace across America, and started the *Bunion Derby*. It is reported that the first race had nearly 300 participants attempting to run 3,455 miles for a $25,000 first place prize. Much like a modern-day event, Pyle pioneered the use of support teams and checkpoints – and also had a rolling shoe repair vehicle following the runners. Twenty year-old Cherokee Andy Payne was the first to cross the New York finish line, winning by more than 15 hours.

There is a history of women not being allowed into the sport of running. Though the modern Olympics were founded in 1896, it wasn't until 1928 that women were allowed to compete in athletic events. Reports after the 800-metre race of exhaustion, prompted the Olympic committee to remove the event from the programme and it wasn't reinstated until the 1960 Rome Olympics.

The civil rights movement in the US contributed significantly to women's opportunities. The Civil Rights Act of 1964 prohibited discrimination in employment on the basis of race, colour, national origin, religion and sex. In 1966, Bobbi Gibb, a female amateur runner, was refused entry to the Boston Marathon, receiving a letter from the race director stating that women were *not physiologically able to run a marathon*. At the time, the Amateur Athletics Union prohibited women from running further than one and a half miles. Ignoring their decision, Gibb travelled to Boston for the race and, after hiding near the start line, joined the field, completing the race in 3 hours, 21 minutes and 40 seconds.

In 1967 Kathrine Switzer became the first woman to run the Boston Marathon as an officially registered competitor, after having reportedly been told that women couldn't run events like the marathon because their features would turn manly and their uteruses would fall out. Although the official rule book had no gender-specific rules, it had been a men-only race until that point. When Kathrine signed up as K. V. Switzer, as she typically did for races, the officials assumed it was a male entry.

During her run, race manager Jock Semple repeatedly assaulted Switzer, trying to grab her bib number to stop her competing. After knocking down Switzer's trainer and fellow runner Arnie Briggs when he tried to protect her, Semple was shoved to the ground by Switzer's boyfriend, Thomas Miller, who was running with her, and she completed the race. It was not until 1972 that the Amateur Athletics Union lifted the one-and-a-half-mile restriction and the Boston Marathon allowed women to compete officially. In the same year, six women were allowed to run the New York City Marathon on the condition they start 10 minutes before the men. At the gun, they sat down in protest. Only in 1984 did the Olympic Games allow women to compete at the marathon distance.

Most marathon participants in 2018 were in the USA with 456,700, of which 43% were women.

There are two main types of ultra-running events, those that cover a specific distance or route and those that cover the most distance in a predetermined period of time. The most common distances are 50km, 50 miles, 100km and 100 miles, although there are also double marathons, 24-hour races and multi-day races of 1,000 miles or longer. Both the format and courses of these events vary, ranging from single loops (some as short as a 400-metre track) to point-to-point road or trail races, to long-distance cross-country events where you navigate and pick your own route.

Many ultramarathons, especially trail events, have significant obstacles, such as elevation changes and rugged terrain. These races are run on dirt roads, mountain paths and paved roads. Usually, but not always, there are aid stations situated every 10 to 20 miles along the route, allowing runners to replenish food and drink supplies or take a short break. There are some self-supported ultramarathon stage races in which each competitor has to carry all his or her supplies including food to survive the length of the race, which is typically a week long. An example of this is the Grand to Grand Ultra in the USA.

Although ultra-running may still be a decidedly niche sport, participation increased 445% in the 10 years up to 2018 from 137,234 to 611,098.

Scott Jurek is one of America's best-known ultra-runners and perhaps most famous outside the US for running with the Tarahumara Indians in Mexico, as chronicled in Christopher McDougall's 2009 book *Born to Run*. The distances the Tarahumara Indians run on a regular basis made me wonder why we don't. Before I read this book I didn't question our limitations and I didn't know what the human body could be capable of. I wasn't aware that it was possible to run such vast distances. It made me think: maybe we set our limits where we think they should be instead of where they could be? Because I was influenced by everything around me, I had no idea where my limitations actually were.

100-mile races are becoming more popular every year. I think people like a challenge that presents a high chance of failure. A challenge with a small chance of failure is not much of a challenge.

LESSONS LEARNED

We all have dreams. But in order to
make dreams come into reality, it
takes an awful lot of determination,
dedication, self-discipline, and effort.

JESSE OWENS, LEGENDARY AMERICAN TRACK STAR

What does running an ultra feel like? At some stage in one of your first ultras you will find that you have a choice: lie down and die (actually get picked up and shuttled back to base), or acknowledge and eat the pain. It is hard to comprehend what you are made of until you are in the depths of suffering on a road that appears to have no end.

You know that finishing a race like this is a victory. What you don't know is at what cost. When you see people who have missed cut-off times being pulled from a race, they exhibit total distress. When you might think they would be relieved to be able to rest. Yet their race did not start hours earlier, but years. Years of planning, training, racing and dreaming got them there, only to be disqualified for being too slow.

Upping from 100km to 100 miles involves a considerable jump, but a jump that I thought I could make. In my first attempt it felt like I had eyed up a river crossing and misjudged the distance. I ran and jumped but instead of landing on the opposite bank I landed, out of my depth, in fast-flowing water.

I was unprepared but I thought I could wing it because I had previously run a 100km. During the preceding four months of training I had surgery and was out for seven weeks. Yet somehow the optimist in me said, *Don't worry about that, go on, do it, you'll be fine.* I learnt the hard way, and I remember it well, every moment of it. It was an experience I hope I never either repeat or forget. I now look back and I'm amazed that I didn't suffer a serious injury. 100km is 62 miles, and the extra 38 miles are unforgiving.

Try and remove your ego from the mix. To be an endurance runner you need to be brave and you can't be brave without being vulnerable. When you decide to take risks, you must be prepared to fail. These failures build you and remake you a stronger person. Running keeps our hearts and minds strong and our bodies healthy. It can give you a connection to the planet and has the power to bring about personal reflections, confessions and self-analysis, solicited or not. There is a lot of emotional vulnerability due to the extended time spent with oneself in stressful circumstances. Best to warn your crew.

MY FIRST 100-MILE ULTRA

*Attitude is the difference between
an ordeal and an adventure*

UNKNOWN

Belfast 2 Dublin, Ireland, 30–31 March 2018

Ignorance is bliss. In certain circumstances that is indisputable, but in other circumstances ignorance is unforgivable.

On paper I was ready. I had followed the training plan (except for the seven-week break). I felt I had the groundwork done. I mean, how ready could one be? At the time I wasn't aware of the part my head had to play in making this race a success and I hadn't done the headwork. Turned out, I hadn't done the legwork either.

The start of the race, all lined up outside a pub in Belfast, I was so full of optimism and positivity. The starting hooter sounded at 12 noon and in my head I told myself I just had to keep moving forward and I would make it. When we got to eight miles, there were 99 miles to go. Somehow, counting backwards in double digits instead of triple digits made me feel like I had broken the back of this race. Even writing this now, I laugh at my own innocence.

For the next 33 miles I felt reasonably comfortable. There are a lot of hills in the first 30 miles and I think the downhills were starting to cause a burning sensation in my feet. At mile 42 I stopped and stripped my feet only to see the beginnings of a blister. I was worried but not overly. It was hurting slightly but, having never had a blister before, I thought I could run through it. About five miles later, having come through the town of Newry, I crossed the Irish border. This gave me a great lift. There are no soldiers or border posts these days so I could only tell by the road signs, which change from miles in Northern Ireland to kilometres in the Republic. However, the good feeling wasn't enough to block out the growing stinging pain on the sole of my foot. I tried to box it and put it somewhere in my head where I didn't have to look at it but this was becoming increasingly difficult.

Fifty-two miles from Belfast I ran into a town called Dundalk. It was after midnight and the start of Fiona's birthday. Jem had a candle ready and he said he would find something to put it into. When I climbed into the car he had put the lit candle in a protein ball. We sang happy birthday, exchanged cards; I ate the protein ball, got out and continued running.

A few miles on, I entered a stretch of road in a place called Castlebel-lingham, a long and straight stretch where you can see for miles. It was dark and very cold. I had nothing left except pain.

I could see the lights of some runners maybe a mile or two ahead and similar about a mile behind. At a petrol station that was closed for the evening, Fiona had set up a feeding station for me. She had heated soup and I sat on a bench wrapped in a duvet, frozen, my spirit broken. My mind couldn't stretch beyond the immediate task at hand. For some time, there was only soup, exhaustion and misery. I wondered whether, if I carried on, would I live? I wondered if I cared. I now know from experience (though I didn't know this at the time) that my head had given up first. My head was telling me anything that I needed to hear in order to stop.

I said to Fiona, *The blisters are now covering both feet, I can't do this anymore, I'm done.* She packed the car, didn't even look at me and drove off and waited a mile down the road. When I got there, with my face contorted in pain, she said, *You said you were done yet you made it another mile,* and then she drove off and did the same again.

At mile 65 I was lying on the path at the side of the road. Fiona had called ahead for a medic. There was no traffic. It was somewhere between

5 and 6 a.m. on a Saturday morning. I was on my back, looking behind my head at a hairdresser's window while a medic examined my feet. The lights were on in the hairdressers and a few people were getting a haircut. I thought, *This can't be right, who gets their hair cut in the middle of the night in a one-street town in the country?* I thought I could be hallucinating. I wondered if I had been hit by a car. It was almost a comforting thought because you can't carry on if you have been hit by a car. But I hadn't been hit by a car.

A bubbly woman, who told me she worked in the Royal Victoria Hospital in Belfast, said, *Your race is over.* For a moment I thought, *Brilliant, I have my out.* But instantly my attitude changed. The consequences of not finishing hit me. *No, I think I will be okay,* I said. The race director was also there. He sported a beard and a long padded coat, like something an Irish rugby player would wear after substitution. He looked cosy and from where I was lying he loomed like a giant. He didn't strike me as the kind of person who smiled very often, though I have to say my judgement of anyone or anything was not to be trusted at that point. I had hit the wall miles earlier when the blisters covered both feet, but each time Fiona had driven off I had been able to carry on. I didn't want to take the out being offered to me here because I knew I had it in me to continue. Even if in pain and even if I had to walk to finish it.

I realised that when I'd thought I couldn't make another step, I had been wrong. I was forced to carry on and I was in bits but I was okay. I said, *If I can't run it, I'm going to walk it.*

The race director said, *Yes, you might make it before the cut-off time.*

I knew immediately how much I preferred the suffering of the final 42 miles to the internal shame of giving up. Having been in and out of court for years fighting to get more custody of my children, I was sick to the teeth of losing. I just wasn't going to do it anymore – I was never going to give up, ever. I wanted to stop right there but somehow I couldn't. Everything was connected and whatever I needed to cope, I would find. Later, I would look back on that moment and realise that my personal life was strengthening my mental fitness. I had always thought it would be the other way around.

I got up and set off again. Even with my feet wrapped I could feel liquid and blood squirt up my ankle. On that walk I got great support. Despair never settled in as my son Jem walked 21 miles with me, talking and keeping my mind off my feet. My friend Laura pulled up beside me outside a town I didn't recognise and drove alongside me smiling and chatting, further lifting my spirits. At another stage Emma was waiting for me and we spent an hour walking together.

Around the 100-mile mark I began to not care if I finished or not. I couldn't remember why I was doing this in the first place. I came across two runners sitting at the side of the road who had given up. I said, *Come on, it's only seven miles to the finish*. One answered, *I don't give a toss*.

I didn't argue because I knew exactly how he felt. I didn't care either, but I kept moving because I knew Fiona and Jem had put so much effort into getting me to the finish line and I was meeting my daughter Chris around the 104-mile mark and I felt that I couldn't let them down. At 102 miles my brother-in-law Dave was standing on the side of the road with my niece and nephew, Aisling and Leo. They were so full of energy and bounce, the way only kids of seven and five can be. I so wanted to get into a bush and lie down but again people I cared about were making me put on a brave face and keep moving. Eventually I crossed the finish line at the Guinness brewery in Dublin in the time of 33 hours, 52 minutes and 51 seconds. I got my medal and became part of the 100-mile club. Jem had bought me the souvenir 100-mile club jacket, which I put on and vowed to never take off.

A group of friends were waiting at the finish line. I felt so out of it, at first I didn't even recognise them. Slowly I noticed Sharon, Emma, Carmel and Beibhinn. Jem, Fiona and Chris had parked and were waiting with them at the finish line. I melted into a sea of hugs. We went into the pub and I drank two of the most delicious pints I've ever tasted.

Because I had finished, I felt I could look myself in the eye. I had trouble walking unaided for a few days but I felt incredibly good about myself. I had been through some very dark hours and with help I had made it out the other side. In my private moments, sometimes I go back to that petrol station in Castlebellingham. When immersed in misery I somehow managed to look at pain differently. I vaguely remember telling myself to *Smarten up, you chose this*, and reminding myself that the sun always rises. And it did rise and then it set again before I finished. But it was so dark and painful, I'm not sure if I added those positive memories afterwards.

My wife Fiona is also from Dublin. She has a great sense of humour, is quick to laugh and doesn't shy away from a challenge or speaking her mind. As a marathon runner herself, Fiona has an understanding of the time, work and effort that it takes to commit to a race. The weeks and months in preparation are the main part. The actual race day is just the layer of icing on a very big cake.

That first night of the Belfast 2 Dublin I really pushed it. Fiona knows me well and understands why I do these things. However, if she'd said after that race, *That's it, I'm not crewing for you anymore*, I would have understood. To crew for me and watch the level of suffering that I went through that night and to continue to encourage me must have been challenging for her. I spent a long time somewhere between wanting to cry and wanting to scream yet unable to do either.

I learnt over the near 34 hours of this ultramarathon that, in ultra-running, there is no place for half-arsed preparations. Ultra-running requires total commitment to your training plan, while fuelling, sleeping, resting and recovering enough to avoid injury. Sadly on this occasion, by the time I had realised that my preparations had been nowhere near sufficient, it was too late. My training plan had been way off: my mileage had been nowhere near enough and my headwork hadn't even come into the scheme of things at this point. Unfortunately, the knowledge that comes with your first 100-mile race experience comes after the fact.

I learnt to never enter a 100-mile race unprepared unless I am ready to face the consequences. I look at the Belfast 2 Dublin race as a very painful learning experience. I treasure it for what I learnt about running a hundred miles and what I learnt about myself. I was unprepared mentally and physically and maybe I was foolish to let my feet get so blistered without taking action. Maybe I was a total fool but maybe not, because I know it stands to me now. The truth is, I learnt more from this race than any other I've ever run.

THE BENEFITS,
OR OTHERWISE,
OF ULTRA-RUNNING

The danger of an adventure is worth a thousand days of ease and comfort.

PAOLO COELHO, AUTHOR OF
VERONIKA DECIDES TO DIE

I f you ask any ultra-runner, there is no doubt they will say that running is good for the mind, body and soul.

The heart isn't the only muscle to benefit from regular exercise. The other muscles in your body enjoy exercise too. When you use your muscles, they become stronger. Strong muscles are also a plus because they support your joints and help prevent injuries. Muscles such as biceps, pectorals and quadriceps are called skeletal muscles because they attach to the skeleton to generate motion. Without muscles and tendons holding us together, we are mere skeletons. Exercise can strengthen our muscles and tendons and keep our bones moving. The more regularly I run, the stronger my muscles and tendons become, therefore the stronger my skeleton is held together.

That is all very true about running in general, but somewhere out there is a street called ultra-running and, once you cross that street, I'm not sure if all those benefits listed above apply. Ultra-running can be positive for your mental health and self-esteem. You can experience high endorphin levels leading to feelings of euphoria. What happens next, I'm not sure. Is ultra-running good for your health? I am sure it is for me but I couldn't be sure it is true for everyone. Sometimes you get to see some great views from the tops of mountains, but none that you couldn't have seen by climbing the mountain in your own good time.

So this leads to the downsides of ultra-running. This list is a little longer, although more experienced ultra-runners tend to manage them better. For starters, you can be more susceptible to injury because you are running for longer and there are added dangers when running in the dark. Then there's hydration. Get dehydrated and risk blurred or lost vision, but while staying hydrated you must ration water consumption to avoid exercise-associated hyponatremia. This occurs when runners deplete their body's sodium levels until cells swell and burst. Eating salty foods combats this issue but this must also be done in moderation to avoid digestive distress.

From my experience digestive distress is quite common during ultramarathons. Managing food and liquid consumption is just part of navigating a race of this length. To finish a race as long as 100 miles, runners need to eat little and often but they must keep moving. This causes a wide range of digestive issues from cramps to diarrhoea. Extreme strain on the body can result in low blood sugar which can cause tears and emotional reactions that may take you by surprise. Hallucinations can occur but usually sort themselves out after a period of rest. In addition to overuse injuries, an increased rate of stress fractures are common, and long-distance runners may also experience muscle collapse, blisters, muscle strain, muscle cramps, skin abrasions, exhaustion and light-headedness.

The symptoms read like something you could encounter on any given day in a geriatric hospital ward. The blisters might be replaced with bed sores but it's a frightening reminder that someday we could suffer all these symptoms just doing the basics like pottering around our kitchen or going to the bathroom.

Ultramarathons require discipline, determination, focus and honesty. The runner has to be honest about their own skills and limitations, and the demands of the race. Although fear is a helpful emotion as it signifies a recognition of danger, one needs to enter such a race not with fear but with eyes wide open.

And so, eighteen months after the Belfast 2 Dublin, I started my next 100-miler. This time I took everything I had learned with me.

MY SECOND 100-MILE ULTRA

It doesn't matter whether you are
a lion or a gazelle. When the sun
comes up, you better be running.

ABE GUBEGNA, ETHIOPIAN NOVELIST

Robin Hood 100, England, 14–15 September 2019

We set off at 6 a.m. from a small village called South Wheatley. It was a cool, clear, crisp English morning and 135 of us started, each carrying a backpack with a long list of essentials and water along with our personal hopes and expectations. I don't know how much everyone else was carrying that day but I felt weighed down with baggage.

My eldest sister Grace had been living with motor neuron disease for the previous few years. It's a cruel affliction and she has the most severe strain, bulbar palsy. Over the previous few months she had lost the power to move or speak. Her limbs had started failing and she was fast becoming a prisoner in her own head.

The Monday before the race, Grace went into a coma. We debated going to the race at all. I wanted to run it, regardless. My only method of coping tends to be running. I couldn't sit at home waiting for news. On the Friday we travelled over to Nottingham and I was terrified that Grace would leave us before the race started, even though I would have been relieved that

41

her isolation and suffering were over. If that happened, we were ready to skip the race and fly straight to Düsseldorf, her home. Saturday morning came and with no news I turned off all notifications on my phone. If Grace died during the next 30 hours I didn't want to know. I asked Fiona not to tell me anything until the race was over. As a result, each time I saw Fiona I couldn't help trying, against my will, to read her every movement and expression.

We had 30 hours to get back to the starting line if we were to make the finish time. I know none of us wanted to have to wear the title 'DNF' (did not finish) after putting in so much mental and physical effort, time and pain. I needed to finish almost four hours faster than my previous 100-mile race, but I felt I had trained well and had confidence. The first 20 miles were along a canal and although it was picturesque, the ground was so hard and uneven I found it difficult to navigate. I ran a lot of it on a tractor track. By the time I hit the first feeding station at the 20-mile mark I was delighted to be moving into the forest for the next 60 miles, and out of the narrow groove I had been running in.

This wasn't just any forest. This was Sherwood Forest, once home to a legendary heroic outlaw depicted in English folklore. Set during the reign of Richard the Lionheart, the adventures of Robin Hood and his merry men follow the noble thief as he steals from the rich and gives to the poor. In the thirteenth century, Sherwood Forest covered about 100,000 acres, a fifth of the entire county of Nottinghamshire. Today the core is about 450 acres, and the forest still contains numerous veteran oaks, trees that have been alive for 500 years.

It was a hot day and the forest cover was a welcome relief. It clearly hadn't rained in a while as the ground was rock hard. My feet were sore and my legs were feeling the lack of give in the ground. I felt comfortable most of the day and spent a lot of hours chatting to other runners, sharing stories and parts of our lives.

As the sun set, we had to attach a torch for light. I had only experienced the creepiness of running in a forest in the dark once before, on a 4-mile loop in Enniskillen during the Last One Standing. My strength seemed to leave with the daylight. I struggled for long periods, and the constant moving shadows created by head torches created a show of horrors at times – every demon my mind could conjure up came at me. All the while I took comfort in knowing that I was in the home of Robin Hood.

At one stage, at about 4.30 a.m., just before the sun came up, I got a call to tell me that I had gone two miles off course. Luckily, everyone had to carry a tracker. I headed back to meet a steward who pointed to a gap in the trees that I had missed. As I ran down the hill the daylight burst out from the clouds and about 200 metres away was a feeding station. It was mile 80 and signalled the end of the forest and I felt ecstatic.

Fiona was ready with encouragement and a breakfast of porridge, toast and hot coffee. I was starving as I had hardly eaten during the night. I ate, brushed my teeth and headed confidently into the last stretch. Two miles down the track my enthusiasm crumbled. Back on the hard, uneven ground, moving in something between a shuffle and a walk, my legs stung with pain and my feet hurt from every angle.

There was a woman running in front of me. I had met her several times during the night and we had chatted at various points when we seemed to be running at the same pace. Suddenly she turned left and ran into a field. When I got there several seconds later, I realised she had been running for cover but hadn't made it. She ended up in an open field with an attack of diarrhoea. Having spent 60 miles in the forest and the dark, five miles into the open and she got a belt of diarrhoea – the timing was certainly unfortunate. The best thing I could do was not offer help and keep running. Twenty minutes later she passed me and I didn't see her again for the rest of the race. The following 18 miles were long and painful.

I finished in a time of 28 hours and 45 minutes. Of the 135 who had started, 94 made it back, and I came in 77th. Forty-one did not make it to the finish.

We sat on the grass at the finish line, cheering in the other runners. With one minute to go, a runner appeared at the top of the road and started running down the last stretch. It was about a minute-and-a-half run to the finish line at a push. Everyone who was at the finish line stood up and started shouting, desperately trying to convey the urgency. There was a collective decision that this runner was not going to miss the cut-off time and everyone seemed to throw energy at him as he sprinted flat out. He made it by seconds in what I imagine was an out-of-body experience.

Although I felt happy to have made it within the time, I knew that my planning had been off. *Why did I run out of energy in the last 20 miles? Why had long stretches during the night been so painful?* I think I knew the answer. I hadn't managed my calorie and water intake properly throughout the night and it had hurt me.

I was overjoyed and disappointed at the same time. During the night I had convinced myself that I could finish within 24 hours. I had learnt a lot and I felt that I now knew things that would have helped me greatly had I known them 30 hours earlier. The benefit of experience, I think they call it. My legs were badly cramping and I was pretty sure that was partly due to being dehydrated. I added hydration and nutrition to my chart.

Once the excitement had passed, we packed up and headed towards home. There was no news from Düsseldorf. We had arranged to spend that night with my nephew Kelvin, who was studying in Wales. It was a two-hour drive and once we set off, the rain started to pour down. It rained so heavily the motorway came to a standstill, so we pulled off to look for a coffee shop.

I exited the car from the passenger side and started to walk with Fiona towards the coffee shop but, having been sitting in the car for a while, my legs had stopped working. There was a grassy mound between me and the entrance, less than a foot tall yet I couldn't get my foot up on it. It was too wide to contemplate going around so I persevered. I even tried climbing it backwards. I thought I heard laughter but I couldn't pinpoint where it was coming from. It was hard to tell in the rain. As it turned out it was Fiona, in stitches, watching me.

I asked, *What's so funny?*

You just ran a 100-mile off-road race, she said, *and now you can't even step up a grass verge.*

We drank coffee and giggled, both of us exhausted.

FOOD IS MORE THAN CALORIES – IT'S FUEL

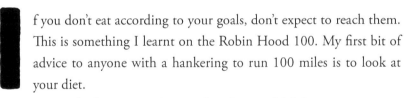

The primary reason diseases tend
to run in families may be that
diets tend to run in families.

MICHAEL GREGER, AUTHOR OF *HOW NOT TO DIE*

f you don't eat according to your goals, don't expect to reach them. This is something I learnt on the Robin Hood 100. My first bit of advice to anyone with a hankering to run 100 miles is to look at your diet.

Anyone who knows me, knows that this wouldn't be a true account of what got me to run ultramarathon distances without a mention of food. In my first book, *The Plant-Based Runner*, I go into a lot of detail about starting out running and the part diet played. The changes I made to my diet probably had a bigger impact on my health than taking up running did. If you were to ask my friends and family to describe me in a sentence or two, I bet they would all mention that 1. I run and 2. I'm a 'fussy' eater.

I was at a friend's wedding recently and had the most glorious experience. I only had to mention to the waiter that I was coeliac and vegan and the most delicious food appeared before me, without any fuss. When it came to dessert I wasn't expecting anything. I didn't mind; I rarely eat dessert as it's usually creamy and I also avoid sugar, but the chef had prepared a gorgeous raw vegan cheesecake. If only all restaurants had those choices on offer. When you make big changes to your diet, you may find it easier to avoid these social situations where you have to ask a lot of questions, only to end up feeling like the awkward one at the table and hoping that the chef isn't going to 'interfere' with your soup. Instead, I have sought out the restaurants that suit me and, when planning a night out with friends, suggest them instead.

Although Fiona isn't coeliac, she has chosen to follow a gluten-free diet since we got together – well, most of the time. Sometimes a sourdough loaf will get the better of her. I can only speak from my experience and say that, over the years, Fiona and I have explored changes to our diet simultaneously. We haven't always made the same changes at the same time, but by sharing interesting things we've read in books or seen in documentaries, we've more or less ended up in the same place. We've made some big, quick, dramatic changes at times, but the evolution of how we eat is a continuing process and this slow, gradual approach over years has been sustainable for us.

From the time I took up jogging I struggled. I huffed and I puffed up and down my local streets to the park. I tried everything I could think of that might make it a bit easier. I remember one of the first things I bought was a pair of men's running tights. I read somewhere that they were the business for running on cold winter nights. I wanted to be associated with anything that was known as 'the business'. I bought the first pair I saw. At that time I was only jogging at night for fear of being spotted by anyone who might recognise me. I tried them twice and I'd say I was quite the sight. An overweight, out-of-shape, 46-year-old male running around the neighbourhood in the dark in a pair of tights, I'd say I raised a few comments alright, none of which were 'the business'.

I tried buying new shoes and different running tops. They were all good encouragement to leave the house but none made the running any easier. Eventually I started to monitor what I ate on the days I was going out jogging. At that time all runs were tough but some were merciless, so when I had a particularly difficult run, I took note of what I had eaten the night before. A pattern emerged very quickly. If I ate meat, I could get a stitch anything up to three days after. So I stopped eating meat. I noticed a difference right away. My big 46-year-old body felt good with no meat in it. I started to lose weight immediately. When I stopped eating meat along with regular jogging, my body shape started to change for the better.

My three children had always been vegetarian so there was a lot of encouragement. It usually came in the form of questions like *Why did it take you 46 years to stop eating animals?* or *How does it feel to no longer be a meater?*

Well, it felt good. Just by not eating meat I lost a pound a month, every month, for two years or three. I say two or three as now that I was running regularly, I was losing weight anyway. Now I was starting to get fit – very slowly, but compared to a few years earlier I was making real progress. I had gone from 108kg to 89kg. Being 19kg lighter made me feel totally alive. I hadn't realised how many things I had shied away from. I found myself jumping on the trampoline with the kids and helping out with coaching at their many sports activities. Even the little day-to-day things like going up the stairs or getting in and out of the car felt better.

About 12 months into my life without meat I ran the Dublin Marathon. I promised myself that, if I finished, as a treat I would go to the local steak-house and order what had once been my favourite meal: steak and a bottle of wine. I did finish and a few hours later I was tucking into a steak. If I had just settled on a bite it might have quenched my cravings. Instead, I ate the whole steak and felt sick and miserable long afterwards. It was days before my gut forgave me and felt good again. I haven't eaten meat since.

Around that time my knowledge about nutrition was also slowly gaining momentum. My methods were very basic. To stop eating animal products was an easy move, but replacing it with healthy, tasty food was a long, slow process. I was used to the meat or the fish on the plate being the centre, and I found it was as much a mental challenge as it was a change to my palate to plate up a meal without it. I was used to cooking simple vegetarian meals for the kids, but if I wanted anything more sophisticated, I needed assistance. Fiona switched to plant-based at the same time, so together we bought new cookbooks and shared the cooking. At least we had each other to bounce ideas off.

When I tried new foods I monitored how well they suited me by how I felt when running. If I felt terrible, I dropped them. If I felt good, I kept them. Over time it got easier to know what to cook and how to make food taste good. The process of switching from being a 'meater' to eating a wholefood, plant-based diet was just as hard as it was to take up running. Thankfully, 11 years later, I still practice both and I have never felt better in my life.

The first training plan I purchased was from Matt Frazier at *No Meat Athlete*. I saw that there were vegan athletes out there pushing their bodies to places I hadn't dreamt of. I got inspiration from them and confirmation that what I was attempting to do was recognised as a thing. Being a plant-based runner was clearly working for me, and it was comforting to know that it was also working for others.

The roll call of world champion sport stars that have chosen a plant-powered diet continues to grow year on year and includes:

- ▶ Venus Williams, tennis champion currently holding 23 Grand Slam titles
- ▶ Novak Djokovic, tennis champion currently ranked number one and holding 18 Grand Slam titles
- ▶ Lewis Hamilton, seven-time world champion Formula 1 driver
- ▶ Scott Jurek, ultra-runner with achievements including seven consecutive wins of the Western States 100-mile Endurance Run (1999–2005)
- ▶ Fiona Oakes, distance runner currently holding four world records for marathon running
- ▶ Meagan Duhamel, two-time world champion pair skater and Olympic gold medallist

From my experience it is common for ultra-runners to be vegan. I don't think I would have been able to make the step up to ultra-running if I hadn't first switched to plant-based eating. My body wouldn't have been up for it.

One of your most important areas is race-day food. No two people appear to need the same. I have seen people tuck into everything imaginable during a race, including gin. I have also seen people in severe trouble from what they have eaten. When you get it right you are usually in for a good day. When you get it wrong, it's not pretty. Although there are several ultras where you must carry your own food and water, in all that I have entered your crew are on hand to prepare your food at each of your rest stops.

One time I was running the 100km race in the forest of Portumna. Fiona had several options ready at each stop: slices of apple with peanut butter, small potatoes and salt, toasted sandwiches with vegan sausages, watermelon, and many more. If a food caused a pain in my gut, I stopped eating it. At one point nothing was digesting well and Fiona was drinking soup from a local food van. It turned out to be gluten-free so I tasted it. It was so good and my body felt so strong that I ate nothing else for the next 40km until the end of the race. I now use vegetable soup as my main food source during every ultra.

During my training for the Connemara 100 I came across dolmades, rice wrapped in vine leaves. Oh, they were so good for me. I liked the taste and I had no issues running straight after stuffing three or four into my mouth. They were 75 calories each and my target was to eat 300 calories per hour and drink 500 ml of water or water and electrolytes. The race took me 27 hours and 37 minutes and I interspersed these parcels of rice with soup. I must have eaten at least 50 or more dolmades before I crossed the finish line. They worked really well for me; my gut thanked me and they gave me plenty of energy and no cramps. It's all about practice, practice and practice. Find what works for you and test it weekly before you put it to a severe test like an ultra.

When training, you need to recover from long runs quickly. There are no weeks off in this 24-week programme leading into a race. After every long run, and every time I feel sore muscles (which can be often), I take protein powder. If it's in the morning I treat it as breakfast and blend oats with seeds, cacao powder, cacao nibs, cinnamon, banana, peanut butter and a vegan protein powder mixed with water or rice milk. If it's in the evening I blend a scoop of protein powder with rice milk and drink it. I know it works because my muscles tell me. Sometimes I really don't feel like it, but

I always take it. If I don't, I am likely to wake the following day with sore muscles and joints.

My weekend when training always includes a long run, which could be anything from 20km to 50km, followed by a recovery protein drink within one hour of finishing. I make sure not to miss any meals on the weekend of a long run even if I don't feel like eating.

A general anti-inflammatory tonic is excellent at giving your system much-needed support. I mix apple cider vinegar with cinnamon, cayenne pepper and turmeric, some warm water and a bit of maple syrup. Finn, who runs my local health food shop, The Hopsack in Rathmines in Dublin, taught me this some time ago and I use it religiously now when in training.

Porridge is my go-to breakfast before a long run, or on race day. Oats are full of fibre and release carbohydrates gradually. Due to this slow release, energy levels are kept consistent throughout your workout, meaning you can train harder for longer. They also contain a number of B vitamins, which help convert carbohydrates into energy.

I'm also a big advocate for having a vegetable smoothie daily. Getting all those veggies into you in one dose is a great way to ensure you're obtaining enough in your diet. For many years I juiced vegetables (rather than blend them in a smoothie) as the added benefit is the speed and ease with which the nutrients enter your system. However, a lot goes to waste and I have found the smoothies give me exactly what I need, right away.

The greatest obstacle to overcome when you start running is not necessarily having strength in your legs. For me, I had the strength to jog three miles but not the lungs. I transitioned to a plant-based diet over time. Increasing the vegetables, fruits, whole grains, nuts and legumes in my diet and substituting the space left by meat or fish or eggs with tofu or falafels or homemade vegetable burgers. Cow's milk was replaced with plant-based milks like soya and rice milk and I could even recreate that cheesy flavour with alternative dairy-free options like nutritional yeast. Within a few weeks of giving up dairy products I was noticeably starting to breathe better. With stronger lungs I could jog for longer. My little world of jogging was opening up into a world of running. If the benefits had not been so great, I would have gone back to my old ways countless times.

Antioxidants, found in colourful fruits and vegetables, are good for everyone but especially athletes as they help reduce inflammation. This is beneficial for endurance athletes who are constantly putting their bodies under pressure by running hundreds of miles a month. Plant-based diets also tend to be lower in fat and higher in fibre. When endurance training, a plant-based diet gives me energy and makes me feel good. Whenever possible I eat high-quality, organic food.

A high-quality diet, by definition, tends to treat you well, giving you energy and reducing your risk of sickness. That doesn't mean that you have to live like a monk. Get used to asking yourself, *Does this food help me or hurt me?* It is important to remember that what suits me may not suit you. We are all different. Do your own experimenting and follow your gut.

For endurance runners, food is more than simple nutrition; food is fuel. Sometimes the timing of food intake can affect your performance. It is important to know your own body and this can only be done by trial and error. Good food will help you train hard, recover quickly and adapt more effectively with less risk of injury.

At the back of this book I have included recipes for the meals I eat regularly when I am training. They are easy to prepare, totally delicious and, most importantly, make me feel good when I eat them.

A GLUTTON FOR PUNISHMENT OR ON A QUEST TO FIND MY LIMITS?

All it takes is all you got.

MARC DAVIS,
LAS VEGAS RAIDERS OWNER (NFL TEAM)

I don't remember how long I was back home before I got a craving to run another 100-mile race. One day it was just there and I didn't know where to put it.

I felt good and I wanted to plan something exciting.

I had read about the Comrades Marathon in South Africa. This is the world's oldest ultramarathon with the largest number of participants, run over approximately 90km between the inland capital of KwaZulu-Natal province, Pietermaritzburg, and the coastal city of Durban. The race route alternates – uphill one year followed by downhill the next. I had heard that at the 12-hour cut-off time, a hooter goes and the gate is closed and the lights turned off. If you haven't finished, you may as well go home as they pull a barrier across the line. You can always come back next year. It wasn't a 100-miler, but it certainly sounded exciting.

After entries opened for 2020, it was five days before I got around to sitting down at my laptop and entering. To my astonishment it was sold out, all 27,500 places. I thought maybe that was a sign that I shouldn't be going to South Africa in 2020. I had been avoiding looking at the Connemara

100 just a few hours' drive from my home, less than 300km away compared to the 14,000km to Comrades. I have been to Connemara many times and I could not recall any section that was flat. The average participation fluctuated between 30 and 50 runners. I took a deep breath and booked a place. A few months later, due to the COVID-19 pandemic, Comrades was cancelled. With the small number booked into Connemara, it was given the go-ahead.

MY THIRD 100-MILE ULTRA

When you put yourself on the line in
a race and expose yourself to the
unknown, you learn things about
yourself that are very exciting.

DORIS BROWN HERITAGE,
AMERICAN LONG DISTANCE RUNNER

Connemara 100, Ireland, 8–9 August 2020

To give myself the best chance of running 100 miles and finishing in a time
that I would be proud of, with six months to go Fiona and I took a few
days off and drove to Connemara to check out the route. With Fiona as my
main crew, it seemed like an opportunity to spend some time together out
of Dublin and view the course at the same time. Romance, relaxation and
some running was the plan.

The first thing to catch my eye as we arrived in Connemara was the
breathtaking scenery. I have only seen natural beauty like it in Cape Town,
South Africa, and the Grand Canyon in the USA. For me, the benefit of
driving the route was to see it and feel it so I could visualise it during my
training. Another was to track the gradient so I knew what to expect.

When we arrived in our hotel in Connemara, COVID-19 was just
flexing its muscles in Ireland. Restrictions were announced and hotels were
told to close. We had booked two nights in one hotel and a further night in
another. Our first hotel closed down after our first night.

On our first day I managed to run a few miles of the route. It was a bit of a wake-up call as it confirmed Connemara doesn't do flat. We moved a day early to the second hotel and managed one night before it also closed down. While we were eating breakfast, we watched all the staff go into a meeting to be told they were out of a job. I felt for all the non-European Union staff, which was most of them, as they wouldn't qualify for any government COVID-19 assistance. We managed to drive 70 of the 100 miles before heading back home to Dublin to a lockdown.

Suddenly, life was in abeyance. No-one knew how serious COVID-19 was going to be. We were restricted to staying within 2km of home and there was uncertainty everywhere. For those first few weeks my training seemed very unimportant. But, at least I was armed with the information to sit down and put a training plan in place. We live on the edge of the Dublin Mountains so, once restrictions were loosened, I started to use them.

The training included hills at least once a week, preferably on the long run. The total elevation for the race was 1,313 metres, so I had to be ready. I mapped a 30-mile route tracking the River Dodder – from my house down to the sea and back up to the mountains – with a climb of almost 300 metres. This was to be one of my regular weekend runs.

I often read a message that I wrote to myself after my first 100-mile race. The message was simple and direct in case I ever decided to attempt this type of race again. It reads, *Be afraid, be very afraid.* Good advice, I think. In the lead-up to the Connemara 100, I regularly woke during the night and stayed awake until the alarm went off at 6.30 a.m., and all I could think about was what could go wrong.

As race day approached, I thought, *I know there will be pain and I think I'm prepared for that.* I also thought, *I feel like I'm charging into this like I'm on a freight train I can't get off and I am afraid.*

I recalled my previous two 100-mile races and I went over them in my head to identify the mistakes I'd made in order to eliminate them. I had been training hard and trying to get into the right frame of mind. I knew from experience that if the suffering hit a tipping point, I would have to keep enough composure in reserve to know the difference between pain and injury. Having said all that, I would try to avoid both. I knew how, in theory. Make sure your training is complete and have confidence in your plan. Eat and drink enough to fuel and hydrate yourself for 100 miles. Pray. And maybe pray some more.

Three weeks to go and the plan was working. My final weekend of pushing out the long runs arrived: 31 miles on Friday, 18 miles on Saturday, rest day Sunday. Listening to audiobooks is something that keeps me company on long runs. Getting lost in a story is a great place to be – the miles can pass without you noticing. On the second day of long back-to-back runs I was tired, close to exhausted and a bit more raw and emotional than I might normally be. I was listening to *The Beekeeper of Aleppo*, a novel by Christy Lefteri. I hit a passage in the book which resulted in a very disturbing rape scene. My regular defences were not doing their job. Tears flowed down my cheeks. I was grateful for the rain. Next time I knew to switch to some music when exhaustion hits.

From there on in I was tapering. Tapering is a strange animal; as your miles are suddenly cut, you can be left wondering what to do with all your energy. I spent my eight hours of running at the weekend measuring the amount of calories that I could eat and the amount of millilitres of water that I could drink. As always, the race would come down to strength, physical and mental, and I was not taking any chances. When the glucose levels drop, normal thinking can become fuzzy. Regular calorie intake from food can help postpone this, hopefully until the last few hours of the race.

I had my first experience of this during the Venice Marathon. I was on time to hit my target when I crossed the Ponte della Libertà, or Liberty Bridge. Once off the mainland and onto the islands of Venice there were only about four miles to go. Due to stomach cramps, I had stopped taking food and gels an hour before. At first sight of the beauty of the city my legs buckled and I felt sick. Nothing to do with the city; it was mile 22 and I'd hit the wall. My energy evaporated and I thought about throwing myself into one of the small boats that dappled the water and floating away. I really didn't want to be there anymore. I was unable to think straight.

On the second to last weekend before the Connemara 100, I got up at 3 a.m. on Saturday morning and ran 13 miles. I was trying to create an ultra situation of being tired, miserable, cold and still running through the dark. It was a lovely night, unfortunately, a beautiful, calm summer night and at 3.30 a.m. the city was alive. On the few miles down to the canal I passed two rocking house parties. On another street I heard a woman who sounded like she was on the phone beside an open window, almost shouting as she told someone all about her boyfriend. I was tempted to listen in for a few minutes but I was on a mission. On the canal there was a crowd of homeless people singing and laughing. It looked like fun. A few of them looked at me like I had lost the plot. It wasn't the first time I had been on the receiving end of strange looks; running around in the middle of the night does that to you. I had 10 miles planned but, due to the calm conditions, I added another few. I was down on the beach as the sun was coming up, and it was magical. Not *quite* what I set out to achieve.

The following day I met two friends, Marie and Ashling, for an 11-mile mountain run. It was tough and became fun when they realised that I had measured it incorrectly and we still had half a mile to climb to reach the top. The slagging I got lasted a month.

I felt very grateful that I had got this far uninjured, yet a bit nervous. The harder I train, the harder my demons train. It seems totally unfair. With three days left I made a trip to Decathlon, Dublin's latest sports superstore, and purchased the last few items for the race, a waterproof lightweight jacket and a few boxes of salt tablets. I was trying to turn my nervous energy into something positive. I had been watching 100-mile-race documentaries but it didn't seem to be working. With their focus on young, professional and incredibly talented sportspeople, I might as well be watching a lunar landing for all the relevance they had to me, a man in his late fifties running his third 100-mile event.

I wondered if I should buy a hat. The weather forecast for Connemara was a hot, sunny 17°C for Saturday. I would be running from 6 a.m. to sundown so this was a concern. It could be worse, the forecast could have been for torrential rain and wind. As Connemara is on the Atlantic coast, it can rain at a moment's notice. It's a bit like Boston, where they have a saying, *If you don't like the weather, wait a minute.* The route goes through the Twelve Bens mountains, which can create a lot of wind, so I obsessed over the choice of hat. I knew it was a bit ridiculous, but I was aware that if I dropped the idea of the hat my mind would wander to more sinister worries. So I ran with it, pun intended. I called into the local running shop on my way home from work and chatted through the pros and cons of every running hat before buying a very thin Nike dry fit cap.

I got home and started to pack. It seemed like I had a lot of gear, as I prepared for the worst: heat, cold, sun and rain. That meant 11 regular running shirts (some years it has rained for 30 hours, so regular dry clothes would be welcome), four long-sleeve, three sleeveless, three body armour, four rain jackets, four pairs of shorts, four pairs of running shoes (two Hoka's Bondi 6, one Hoka Clifton, one Asics), five pairs of 1,000-Mile socks. There was a webinar for the runners and crew, as, thanks to COVID-19, the pre-race meeting had been cancelled. Afterwards I took the dog for a walk to try and calm down. As the sun set, we sat by the River Dodder, listening to and watching a waterfall. The sound of running water was soothing and lovely and eased my nerves as I went over the race in my mind. The next morning we travelled to Connemara.

With every hour that passed I grew more panicked. I could feel the weight of expectation – my expectation. I wanted to do well. I was worried that I would somehow let everyone down. Negative feelings were coming at me from everywhere. I started to think that maybe I was out of my depth.

In this race a car has to tail you for safety every mile from mile five. I had a crew of three, and three cars. Weeks earlier I had put out the call to family and friends, and Emma – ever reliable and forever supportive – and my sister Naomi's partner, Alan, had both stepped up to the challenge.

They had all given up a weekend at a good cost just to support me. Their unquestioning loyalty only served to increase my nerves, making me increasingly conscious of failure. *Oh God, what if I don't make it past mile 50?*

Yet chatting with Emma actually helped ease my nerves a little. Together with Fiona we sat down to discuss the race. Afterwards, feeling slightly dizzy, I went to my room and lay down for a few minutes to try and get a handle on myself. It was 8 p.m. the night before the race. By the bed was a card marked 'Jonathan'. Odd, I thought, as I opened it. It was from Fiona:

Jonathan, you are an inspiration to more people than you will ever know. Friends, family, followers & Fiona. You got this AND we got YOU. Never before has the phrase 'We'll be behind you every step of the way' been more true. You have all my love. Take it with you and use liberally, as required. Fiona xxx

I lay on the bed and let it sink in. They had already invested in me, and they had my back. My job was to run at a speed that would get me to the finish in under 30 hours. I had no need to worry about letting anyone down; if that came to pass, I would worry about it then. I felt my strength come back and my nerves diminish, and started looking forward to the run. The power of a note, I thought. I got up and we all went out for a walk.

The race started at 6 a.m. and after all the preparation it felt great to be running. It was going to be a hot sunny day, very unusual for Connemara. As I covered the first 10 miles I felt good and strong and positive. The scenery was breathtaking. By mile 20 things had taken a turn for the worse. I started to feel the strength of the sun. Gradually, no matter how much I drank, I felt too hot. I was slightly weak and my head felt as if it was overheating. I stopped for food and a change of clothes. It was way too early to start feeling down. My crew encouraged me to eat and drink and, after washing myself down with cold water, I soaked my hat.

The first checkpoint was at mile 30. By the time I had reached it, I felt marginally better but still far from my best. Emma, knowing me well from us having trained for and run many races together, noticed that I was struggling and at mile 35 started running with me – long before we had planned. I had eaten too much at the previous stop and I had a cramping pain in my gut, so she ran beside me to make sure I ran slowly until it passed. It made a huge difference. It was unbearably hot and I needed some distraction.

I was afraid of getting diarrhoea. Up until that point I had never experienced diarrhoea when running. Stomach upset can be the result of a number of factors but certainly the constant bouncing movement doesn't help. During a run, your body is prioritising where your blood needs to go. Large muscles, your heart, skin and lungs come first and your digestive system loses out. In fact, blood flow to your internal organs can decrease by up to 80%. A study on *The impact of physical exercise on the gastrointestinal tract*, by Erick Prado de Oliveira and Roberto Carlos Burini, showed that reduced blood flow to the gut is the most significant factor in nausea, vomiting, abdominal pain and (bloody) diarrhoea for athletes, with almost twice as many runners as other endurance athletes suffering from these symptoms.

Now that I was eating more food than in previous races, I was conscious that my digestive system was being given more work to do. In training I had practiced for this, but not for 30 hours straight. I was eating 300 calories per hour and I had to be very careful. Hours earlier I had eaten some hummus and I was in pain for four or five miles. Hummus had never hurt me before, but today it was a no-no. This time I had eaten some oats. It's difficult when you are eating every hour and you are 10 hours in. You want to vary your food, your taste buds are almost begging for something new. I knew a few bites of oats mixed with a banana and peanut butter would be my limit. Yet I ate double what I should have. I felt a bit like a kid knowing that he shouldn't eat too many sweets. Before I could think about it I had shovelled it in. I made a note to not make this mistake again. I spent the following 10 miles running with a gut pain.

Hours later, just as the sun was going down, I could feel a pain on the top of my foot just under where the shoelaces were tied. Within an hour this pain had spread to both feet and was something that I could no longer ignore. My feet had swollen and, even with my laces tied loosely, the pressure of my socks was hurting badly. I waved the crew car down and got a pair of scissors and cut the top of the socks, releasing the pressure.

When total darkness descended, Alan got out of the car and started running with me. He had been a marathon runner 30 years previously but, as far as I knew, due to an injury hadn't run since. If he felt any discomfort or pain he didn't show it.

Apart from one stretch of road about nine miles long, the route was quiet and uninhabited. Peaceful. Throughout the night my head torch lit up the eyes of sheep. Depending on how the light caught their eyes, sometimes they looked like they felt sorry for me. Other times they had the *I just killed my parents* look. I was now shuffling and walking the hills, but I was still moving. All through the night I kept reminding myself, *This body works for me, you will work efficiently until the end.* It gave me a feeling of detachment from brain to body for the hours that I needed it.

By the time Sunday morning came, I had learnt the value of absolute preparation. I had not missed one long run in training and I had planned meticulously. All my food had been tried out on previous runs. I had aimed to consume 300 calories and drink 500ml of water per hour. Due to the heat I was consuming 750ml of water per hour, which was a good sign. It meant I was staying hydrated.

At mile 88, day two was just starting to warm up. It was just after sunrise and Fiona had the last stop ready. I ate my calories, took two salt tablets and had a full shower with a solar-powered shower hanging off a post on the side of the road. Watched by a dozen sheep I put on fresh clothes and shoes. Remarkably, I felt great. I had been running for over 20 hours with a 15-minute sleep (that had felt like four seconds). Emma and Alan took it in turns to run with me until we reached Clifden.

We had agreed that when we got to Clifden, all four of us would run the last three miles to the finish line. I had a strong fear that those last miles could be torturous. As it turned out, it was a remarkable feeling to be accompanied by my crew for those final three miles. The energy was so strong I felt I was being carried. Alan had run a total of 12 miles with me including the last three where he talked me through every step. *Lift your head, keep moving, we are going to hold the pace right up to the next corner.* When we got to the corner, of course he'd say, *Keep moving now, we are going to keep our posture until we get to the garage*, and so on until the finish line appeared.

Finishing strong was something I hadn't dared to dream of. Now it was happening and it felt incredible. I was an hour and 10 minutes faster than my previous time and the terrain in that race had been flat. I was more than five hours faster than in my first attempt. I knew that I had hit on a winning formula. If not literally winning it certainly worked for me. Good planning and preparation and a crew that 'got it', mixed with pacers keeping me company, had worked. Analysis would come later. Now I needed some hugs, hot coffee and sleep.

The day after the race, I awoke feeling great, with no injuries and a wonderful sense of satisfaction. I knew from experience that I had a few days of contentment coming my way. I had not only survived but I had exceeded my goal. I had thought that if I could run the first 80 miles I would be happy to walk the last 20. But I had managed to run most of the race with the exception of some hills that had proven too steep. I had even run the last few miles, which was an absolute bonus I had not anticipated.

Following the race, we set off for West Cork, a four or five hour journey from Connemara. To break it up we planned to take a few nights and ramble down the coast. My stepdaughter Sarah was staying in Kenmare in County Kerry and we dropped in for a night. Here I discovered that my 'no injuries' assessment might have been a bit premature, as by mid-morning one of my toes had started to throb. Within an hour it began to swell. I noticed the base of the nail was infected. An hour later my foot blew up. An hour after that my shin turned red and was sore to touch. I couldn't get a doctor to see me in Kenmare – because of COVID-19 they were only seeing 'regular customers'. I wasn't too put out; I have only been to a doctor twice in the last 30 years, both times after accidents. I tend to take an alternative approach whenever possible.

A number of my running friends are nurses. I made a call and was advised to elevate the leg. I did so, and we headed out of Kerry and continued our trip to West Cork. By this point the toenail was not looking good so I called my sister-in-law, Dee, who would know what to do. Dee works in the health industry and has long been my first call when a health issue crops up. Her knowledge of body systems and the links between diet, supplementation, lifestyle and body/mind health is encyclopedic. I can't remember all the remedies she gave me over those days but the toe needed a lot of TLC. Magnesium sulphate paste was applied a few times a day to draw out the infection, and I had warm foot baths with Epsom salts to support that process. After a few days the infection cleared. Once the toenail lifted the pressure was gone and, a few days later after a night of dancing, the nail fell off. If that was the worst thing to come out of this 100-mile, roughly 215,000-step ordeal, I was grateful. I had suffered worse from running a regular marathon.

I put this down as one of my best races ever. A lot of things came right for me, mainly because I had prepared better than for any other race. I wondered what I could have achieved had I done a pre-season and stretched out my muscles. In order to find out, I added an eight-week pre-season training plan to the chart.

Alan, Emma and Fiona had been an amazing crew. They worked well with each other and constantly calculated where we were and compared it to where we should be. Sometimes the advice was to speed up, other times to relax and eat more calories. When the race was finished the analysis kept coming. A week later we all had a zoom call and shared ideas to make a better, faster, more efficient go of it next time.

It was only one week later and I could feel my excitement rise at the thought of my next attempt in a year's time. In eight weeks, I would hit my 57th birthday, yet I felt better in my body than I had done in 30 years. This was my 21st marathon of 26 miles or over. My first was at age 45. Having a plant-based diet and taking regular exercise was starting to show dividends. I felt gratitude that I was able to take on challenges that would have been out of my league 30 years before.

GET YOUR DUCKS IN A ROW

Mind is everything. Muscle – pieces of rubber.
All that I am, I am because of my mind.

PAAVO JOHANNES NURMI, KNOWN AS
THE 'FLYING FINN', AS HE DOMINATED
MIDDLE-DISTANCE AND LONG-DISTANCE
RUNNING IN THE EARLY 20TH CENTURY

Before you even decide to enter a 100-miler there are a few little things you may want to throw your eye over. This is not the race you enter when you are drunk or trying to impress someone. For most people who take on the demands of running a 100-mile ultramarathon, the challenge involves months and more likely years of endurance runs, nutritional tweaks, training plan variations and race failures. 100-mile finishes are less about genetic talent than about strategic training, long-term planning and desire.

Timing – Make Your Training Count

Runners know the importance of good timekeeping. Have you ever arrived late for a race or missed a time by seconds? One year I was struggling to beat a 4-hour marathon and I missed the time by seven seconds. *That's fine,* I thought, *what's seven seconds?* I told myself it didn't matter, that I should have some fun. But that night I awoke shouting, *Seven seconds!* Apparently my subconscious wasn't as cool with it as I thought I was. Seven seconds can be the difference between joy and misery, as, for that matter, can one second. Once I got home to Dublin I entered the Cork Marathon which was seven weeks away. Instead of resting, I had to train for the next seven weeks then run another marathon, all because I had missed a time by seven seconds. Time is important to runners. Others might have been able to let this go, but once I had set the goal I had to do what I had to do to achieve it. In heavy rain and wind I crossed the finish line in Cork with 20 seconds to spare. When it comes to ultra-running the seconds tend to count for less.

To train for an endurance event you must have discipline and consistency. Clocking up the miles and, with them, time on your feet is the most important part of your training. Having a running watch that can track your training is a valuable tool for analysing your progress. I use a Garmin Forerunner 935 watch. It's my most expensive piece of kit, but is something I rely on. These days, most running watches come with GPS built in and will measure almost everything: pace, speed, heart rate, cadence, stride length, elevation gain, calories, time, distance, etc. I also use a calendar wall chart to mark my mileage, so I can tell at a glance if I am on target.

Support – Who's Got Your Back?

The first thing I would suggest is to get the support of your partner, if you have one. Without this, the next few months might be your last as a couple.

It's a good idea to explain to them what a race like this realistically entails, and what a serious ultra training plan looks like. Time spent out running maybe three or four evenings a week along with three to five hours on a Saturday and Sunday. Time spent in the gym. Early nights, preparation for healthy meals and recovery days. You'll need empathy and understanding should you come down with an injury. In Section Three Fiona gives a detailed description of what it takes to be part of the crew, in *The View from the Crew Car*.

A good open chat might be on the cards along with a weekend away and maybe even some presents. If your partner is not a runner, very big presents. To successfully run a 100-miler you will need full support during the months of training, not to mention help and support on race day. That doesn't even include listening to you talk about it or nursing you after the race.

Fitness – Are You Ready for This?

The minimum starting fitness level for this distance is marathon fit, as 100 miles is a long way. Six to nine months would be a good minimum benchmark for the training to go from marathon to 100-miler, but with completion in mind rather than performance. If you want to run a fast time, figure on 12 to 18 months. You don't simply enter a 100-mile run; you commit to it. That means the training is pretty intense and involves running four to six times a week. For someone ordinary to achieve something extraordinary takes a lot of time and effort. It is achievable, of course, as long as you are willing to do what it takes.

How much are you willing to sacrifice? No weekend late nights for three or four months or, certainly, very few. Very little TV and possibly cutting out a chunk of your social life.

One of the reasons your first 100-miler is so difficult is that a lot of what will or will not work for you will not become apparent until mile 75. What might work at mile 40 may not work at mile 80, and so on. You will only know by doing it. Without experience there is a big leap of faith required. You just need to focus on the training and the preparation.

When your training plan starts, I would advise that you run your long runs slowly. Two 20-milers back-to-back, Saturday and Sunday, would be better than one 50-miler because that 50 will give you a ton of fatigue. Map out your objective. How do I efficiently train? You must break your plan into pieces, knowing every time you do a training run you are placing one piece into the puzzle. You don't need to focus on the end game every day, but it's good to be confident that the overall picture will make your race day successful.

Motivation and Inspiration – What Will Move You When All You Want to Do is Stop?

I am motivated mainly by my children. I would like to inspire them and to let them know that some things are worth fighting for.

I find inspiration from all sorts of places. I am inspired by my regular running friends. A few years ago we all started from scratch and we ran the Dublin Marathon together in 2019. We run, chat, laugh, and eat cake almost weekly. Certain athletic achievements give me great motivation; for example, as an Irishman, David Gillick winning the 400-metre final in the 2007 European Indoor Championships in Birmingham. And Ireland's rugby team beating New Zealand at Soldier Field in Chicago in 2016. The summer of 1960, when Ethiopian Abebe Bikila won gold in the Olympics, the sponsor was Adidas and when Bikila arrived, the shoes he was given didn't fit him. Bikila decided to run the marathon barefoot, the way he'd trained. Bikila became the first black African Olympic champion. I wasn't born for this event but it still inspires me. When Jonah Lomu played for New Zealand against England in the 1995 rugby World Cup, I had never seen anything like him before and to watch him run over Mike Catt to score a try will forever be in my memory. I'm inspired by Katie Taylor, Ireland's most successful professional boxer. Brian O'Driscoll and Trevor Brennan, two Irish rugby players, have given me countless moments. Then there's Sonia O'Sullivan, Irish former track and field athlete, Kathrine Switzer, first woman to officially run the Boston Marathon and Jack Charlton, the Irish coach who led Ireland to our first football World Cup in 1990, uniting a country in celebration, the like of which has never been seen in Ireland before or since.

Motivation and inspiration don't always come from sporting legends. One evening it was bitterly cold outside, dark, raining and a strong wind was swirling around – it was just miserable. I jokingly said to Fiona, *Back soon, I'm off for a run*. I saw her face drop to a look of disappointment. I had forgotten that she had pulled a calf muscle and was laid up for two weeks. When I saw her reaction, I realised how lucky I was to be able to go for a run. I changed and went out. As always, when I got back I felt great.

My sister Grace, suffering from motor neuron disease, has been a prisoner in her own head for the last 18 months. She has no movement except for her eyes. She has no speech and breathes with the help of a ventilator through a tracheostomy. She can only cry. Due to COVID-19 our only contact is a weekly Zoom call. Every time I feel lazy or ungrateful or too delicate to go out and run in a storm I think of Grace.

Travel – Are You Ready to Get Out of Your Comfort Zone, and Your Bed?

I enjoy travelling for a race, especially within or close to the same time zone. I have been using running as a reason to go places that I am interested in but probably wouldn't visit otherwise. Every year I try to run in at least one city that I have never been to before. But, fun as this is, you need to be careful. The minor difficulties you encounter on the road can distract from the thoughts of the task ahead.

One year, five of us flew to Italy for the Venice Marathon. It is one of the most spectacular cities I have ever been to. We flew out there on a Saturday morning, travelled by boat from the airport to our hotel, and just managed to get to the Expo to collect our race numbers. Late that night three of us sat in our hotel room trying to figure out what time to set our alarms for. We had to be at a bus stop at 7 a.m. to get on a coach to take us 20 miles out of Venice to the start line. We knew that Venice was one hour ahead of Dublin but that very night, at 1 a.m., the clocks were to go back one hour to winter time. We were all relying on our smartphones, but without Internet coverage we didn't quite trust them. We hoped that the time would automatically update at 1 a.m. The problem was the three phones each had a different time, 10 p.m., 11 p.m. and midnight. Because we were slightly panicked at the prospect of missing the bus, we couldn't figure it out. We requested a wake-up call from reception. Although it never came, we somehow managed to make the bus.

In October 2017, Fiona and I travelled to Moscow for the marathon. When travelling in Europe, you can often take a guess at what a sign says, but not in Moscow, unless you can read the Cyrillic alphabet. Thankfully, Fiona had learned it and had been listening to the sounds of the letters for the previous few weeks. Travelling to the centre from the airport on the Metro, she could understand the announcements and read the station signs and knew where we had to get off to get to our hotel. Without that homework we could still be travelling the subways of Moscow.

Food – What Fuels You Best?

To put in the effort that is required to complete a training programme, I need to feel good in my own skin. That begins with food. The plan for me is always simple: whole food, plant-based (WFPB). It is difficult to stay away from processed food every day but WFPB is my target. I'm coeliac so I do not eat gluten. A long time ago I gave up refined sugar. I also choose to keep meat out of my diet. To keep my immune system strong I take a daily dose of antioxidants, usually in the form of blueberries, and vitamin C, usually as a supplement.

I try to eat early every evening so that my body has four or five hours to digest food before bed. That way during sleep my body can work for me, healing injuries, strains and sicknesses. Sleep spent digesting food, I believe, deprives the body of cleansing and repair time.

When you are a coeliac you get used to carrying your own food with you everywhere. This is even more important when travelling for a race, even though there is great choice of gluten-free food now compared to 10 years ago. However, nothing beats being prepared. If you are travelling to a race, I suggest bringing what you need rather than relying on being able to get it in unfamiliar surroundings. If a banana and peanut butter on your homemade brown bread is the breakfast that works for you in training, pack them for race day.

Each year I learn more about what foods work for me and what combinations don't. I learn what foods help me recover and what gives me energy, supplements that protect me or speed repair from injury, what breakfast helps fuel the early miles of a long run and what I shouldn't be drinking the night before (the answer here is alcohol). I believe that every bite counts when training. As a rule of thumb, the foods I eat are low sugar, low salt, minimally processed and pass through my digestive system in that ideal 12 to 24-hour timeframe.

How do you do that? There is a simple test to see how quickly your digestion is working. Eat a large serving of beetroot with your meal, taking note of the time and day. Now, keep an eye on your stools, counting the hours until you see the colour change to red. Keep note of how long you continue to see the traces of red. The longer the transit time, the longer the waste is sitting in your digestive tract. A time of 12 to 24 hours is excellent, but it can take up to three to five days to pass food. To improve your transit time, make sure you're drinking enough water and increase your fibre intake.

I have learnt a lot and changed a lot in the last 10 years. 10 years older, a few stone lighter and now a vegan ultra-runner, I run most days. At the same time I try not to take myself too seriously. If the plan falls apart, I get over it, move on and start again the next day. I follow the path that works for me. It's important to find one that works for you.

Tiredness – Where Do You Go When You Can't Go to Sleep?

To run 100 miles, you must first make friends with tiredness. I used to think it was pain, but now I'm sure it's tiredness. Pain is a probable but not a given in a 100-mile race, while tiredness is a given. In my third race I didn't suffer much pain, but in all three I have had to deal with tiredness. Of course, excessive tiredness left unchecked can lead to pain.

For the Connemara 100 in August 2020, my third 100-mile race, five months of training with one or two long runs each weekend meant I was reasonably well prepared. Yet I still suffered fatigue. At around mile 30 I felt the weight of the hot sun on my head and tiredness and weakness got into my body. I ate, drank and soaked my head in cold water until I recovered.

At mile 45 I started to feel tired again. The relentless sunshine wasn't helping. My calories were upped as were my salt tablets and magnesium drinks. At mile 62 I felt full of energy, possibly feeling at my best so far in the race.

At mile 71 I went from full of beans and confidence to shattered. I had no warning; it was dark and thankfully the temperature had dropped from 24°C to 16°C, it was cool, but far from cold. Luckily, my crew noticed that I suddenly started to struggle. A stop was called and I was fed and watered, which enabled me to move on.

Nine miles later, at mile 80, a sleep was scheduled. I had 15 minutes in the front seat of a car. The seat wasn't put back so I couldn't get too comfortable. It worked: I felt refreshed and, after 23 hours of running, ready to go again.

In my first two 100-milers, I had tried to block feelings of exhaustion out by diverting my thoughts. It had never worked. The difference with this race compared to the previous two is that we were all on top of the tiredness; we expected it and we faced it as a team and managed it. We had a plan of action and it worked. If you're running in the dark, the chances are you have already run through the day. This means you are tired, physically exhausted. I always get to a point in a race when I need to rest. However, I do think, when in doubt, keep moving. Sometimes, the longer you rest, the longer it takes you to get going again.

If you have a crew who are willing to run, snap them up. They can pace you when the miles get tough. The more miles that you can be paced, the better. This changed my last 100-mile race from the feeling of Jesus carrying the cross in *The Last Temptation of Christ* to a feeling of enjoyment.

Be Prepared – But Remember, Shit Happens

There's nothing like a 100-mile race to highlight our weaknesses. That goes for personal baggage too. When your demons come for you during the night you had better have your house in order. The continuous grip of darkness can be crushing. You can find yourself in a dark place inside as well as out. It can feel very raw and your mental and physical sides are forced to work as one. Neither can operate independently. Dealing with some things in life can be hard; when you add total exhaustion, darkness and delirium into the mix, you can feel very alone. And you could still be facing another 10 hours of running. This distance can be cruel. That's why psychology is just as important as the physicality of running.

No matter how well prepared you are, you can never be 100% sure how your body is going to react to an endurance event on any given day. Something unexpected could happen. You could go over on an ankle or slip in the rain. In an ultra that possibility moves closer to a probability. It helps to have a good crew who will handle everything that the race throws at you while remaining calm.

In a marathon, they talk of hitting the wall. I know from experience this can be challenging. In a 100-mile ultra you can hit it a second, third and even fourth time. It can feel like death has come for you.

Ticknock Forest lies on the outskirts of Dublin, right where the city meets the mountains. A few years ago I was mountain biking with a friend, Dylan. Once upon a time we were in school together chasing girls and doing teenage things. Now we run or cycle up mountains. Dylan is a seasoned mountain biker and knows his stuff. He had been encouraging me to try biking and we had been out two or three times. It seemed right up my street, physically tough and as dangerous and exhilarating as you want to make it. I was still a novice but I figured if I kept Dylan in my sights I could mimic him and I would be okay. The hard climb up to the top was over and we were two-thirds of the way down the mountain when I lost sight of him. I was travelling at a speed that was thrilling. I thought, *God, I'm good at this.* At that exact moment the universe decided to take me down a peg and the front wheel stuck between two rocks and I was thrown forward.

Time almost stopped as I was flipped in the air and my brain scanned the terrain. I waited and waited and, moving in super slow motion, I braced for impact. Eventually I hit the ground about 15 feet away on a relatively flat section of track, thankfully missing the jagged rocks. I was facedown with my head pointing up the mountain. I had done a twist and a flip before impact. I opened my eyes and lifted my head out of a puddle. I took a breath and moved my legs. Both seemed okay. I slowly rocked my body from side to side; I felt no pain. I started to laugh, I don't know why. The adrenaline rush maybe and the relief of landing uninjured.

Over the next few hours pain started to kick in. Turns out I had broken a few ribs and torn the supraspinatus tendon in my shoulder. This is the part of the rotator cuff that covers the humeral head and controls arm rotation and elevation. So not good. I called Joanne Finn, a friend and a physiotherapist. Slowly she put me back together. For six or seven months I couldn't run. Any movement of my arm caused a pain in my shoulder.

Two weeks after the accident, I was sitting on the side of the bed taking off a sock. It was a bit tight and I strained to remove it. Suddenly I heard a popping sound from inside myself and felt a sharp pain. I rang Joanne and told her. She laughed and told me I had just refractured one of my healing ribs. It would be another six weeks before I recovered from the set-back, providing I didn't have any more sock issues.

Plan – When Race Day Arrives, Be Ready to Succeed

You will learn a lot on race day and hopefully not just the depths of misery that you can go to. You may start this race in the best shape of your life and finish it in the worst. If you are not afraid and nervous, there might be something wrong with you.

For each race, I like to have a game plan. This keeps my mind on the task at hand and prevents me from becoming overwhelmed during the race by trying to think of everything at once. For my first 100-mile race, the Belfast 2 Dublin 107-mile ultra, my race-day plan was:

1. To pace myself.
2. To eat and drink as often as I could.
3. To finish.

Now I look at this differently. I would advise everyone to have a complete race-day plan. A hundred miles is a long run no matter which way you look at it. Keeping yourself together mentally and physically is a full-time, all-consuming job.

For my second 100-miler, the Robin Hood 100, I broke the race into 10 parts. From my house it is five miles uphill to my parents' house and five miles downhill back home. I had run this route many times in training. Often I called in to see my parents and was nearly always met with a smile. During the race, I planned to 'visit' my parents 10 times. Five tough miles, rewarded with a smile, followed by five easier miles. I only had to count to 10. I made sure that in my head I never stepped out of my 10-mile loop. I only ran 10 miles, over and over, so the totality of the 100 miles never became overwhelming. The plan sort of fell apart on mile 90 when I was so exhausted I couldn't even focus on 10 miles. I switched to running one mile at a time.

Along with my game plan I had agreed with myself that the specific aim was to finish within 30 hours. I didn't know what 60 of the miles in the forest would be like, with a possible 40 in the dark. I downloaded several novels and I had a playlist of 100 songs to cater for my every mood. The natural breaks in the race were at mile 20 when we entered the forest, mile 50 after the first forest lap and mile 80 just before leaving the forest. There was a food station at each which was something to look forward to. My game plan was very general. I had a set speed that I wanted to run. I wanted to limit my time spent at food stations to 15 minutes, except for two, where I gave myself 30 minutes. I intended to eat as much as I could take and to drink every hour. What was missing was a strict plan stating what had to be eaten and drunk every hour to maintain strength. Leaving this area unclear was a bad idea.

With a plan written out and discussed for every eventuality that you can think of, you will be taking some of the pressure off yourself and delegating some of the responsibilities. For my third 100-miler, the Connemara 100, I had a crew of three and we talked about the race beforehand. Writing out my race-day plan and goals and sharing them with the crew made a big difference.

My main goal was to finish within the 30-hour cut-off time. I was clear that I wanted encouragement when I was down and, if I wanted to quit, well, unless I was injured that was not an option. I knew that if I quit I would have to face myself for possibly a year until I got to run another

100-miler. We covered situations like when I needed to eat but didn't want to. I had trained long runs eating 300 calories per hour and drinking 500ml per hour. I wanted to stick to this as best I could. How often I was to take electrolytes I left to Fiona to calculate. Much depended on the temperature and how much fluid I was losing. Everything that I could comfortably delegate to someone else gave me extra space to concentrate on my job, which was running.

I felt like we ran this race together and as a result it was my most enjoyable and successful ultra. Due to good race-day planning, preparation and a crew that shared the same goal, I never felt lost or alone, which from my previous experiences I had come to think was part of running this distance. And I had a day I will forever be proud of.

When all the training and preparing is done and race day arrives, I like to organise something for the following day, to let me know that life doesn't start and stop with the race. That helps me keep my nerves in check. I tell myself that what is about to happen is not easy. This is a serious challenge that needs to be respected. If I finish in one piece, I will be mighty proud of myself. If I don't achieve what I set out to do, I will still be here to try again another day. As long as I bow out for a good reason – not *I just wasn't feeling it* – I should be okay.

Success – Hard Work, Preparation and Learning from Your Mistakes

The exciting thing about a 100-mile ultramarathon is that you do not know what will happen. It's also the terrifying thing. It could be the heat, the cold, blisters, your body, your head or many other internal or external factors. For everything to go in your favour over 100 miles is a tall order.

But it only takes a few things to go against you for your race to crumble. So if you went to the trouble to buy and read this, you are clearly not the 'giving up easily' type. You can cover yourself as best you can by taking care of the basics: completing your training programme and eating nutritious food. You can add in night running to get used to the feeling of darkness and exhaustion together. Getting used to eating and drinking during your runs is essential so that when you stand at the starting line, you already know what your body can digest when severely stressed. But there is more to a successful 100-mile race than consistent training and that is exactly what you will learn in Section Two of the book: *The Peak Performance Training Guide.*

The Peak Performance Training Guide

STAND ON THE START
LINE WITH CONFIDENCE

All things being equal, you will have a point in the year where you peak. Being a runner you can't keep your fitness at 100% all year. Even elites only peak for a limited period of time and start each season from scratch, though maybe not the same scratch as you and I might start from. And while we don't want to behave like elites, we want to see their overall plan and take what might work for us. They can prepare for nine months and perform for three. The elite pattern of rest, prepare, perform, rest, prepare, perform is something we want to adopt.

This plan begins with two weeks of rest, followed by six weeks of preseason preparatory work, running at a very low volume and focusing on areas of your body that become overused and lose mobility due to the strains of repetitive running, and finally 24 weeks of running at increasing intensity, culminating in your targeted race.

Alongside the typical weekly runs we have come to expect in a marathon training plan, this plan includes other focus areas, which, when incorporated into your weekly training, will deliver benefits to you both mentally and physically as you undertake this enormous challenge.

First, the Fun Bit

I love looking for races to run. I usually start with a country I want to visit and then, for marathons in particular, a city I haven't been to. My brother

Simon, who lives in South Carolina, has been running for the last two years and is ready to take on his first marathon. He's suggested I travel to the US and we run the Chicago Marathon. This is something that I will look forward to, as I have yet to run a marathon in the US.

In this section of the book, all the work is with a goal in mind. It is 32 weeks of focused preparation and training. If you're not crystal clear on what you're working towards, it's likely to fail. Pick a race you're excited about. You'll be nervous too and that's totally normal.

Once you've picked your race, book it. There's nothing like fixing a date in your diary to focus the mind. Now, while you still have your diary open in front of you, count back 32 weeks. That's your start date for this programme.

WEEK	DURATION	ACTIVITY
1 - 2	2 weeks	Two week rest period
3 - 8	6 weeks	At the start of week three, take the *Mobility Test* and, based on the results, take the recommended stretches and practice them daily for the next six weeks. Also follow the *Integrated Stability Programme* through its progressions for six weeks. Now, repeat the *Mobility Test* to chart your progress.
9 - 32	24 weeks	Depending on your level of fitness, you can follow The *Minimum* or *Advanced Training Plan for your first 100-Mile Race*. Simultaneously, you will be working through the *Peak Performance Chart* on a weekly basis. Both the training plans and *Peak Performance Chart* are suitable for adaptation and personalisation.
You're ready for your first 100-mile ultra		

Weeks 1 and 2: Two-Week Rest Period

I get it. You've picked your race and you're raring to go. But for weeks one and two you're going to rest. Total rest. Walking is the most vigorous exercise you should do in this period. During this time of rest all micro tears, internal strains and injuries have an opportunity to heal. From week three you can start running again at a low level and you can start doing other activities.

Start of Week 3: The Mobility Test and Your Stretching Programme

The *Mobility Test* will take about 10 minutes to complete. This is how you will identify the muscles that are tightest, which are always the ones to work on the most.

Flexibility is a top priority, right after rest, food and water. It even comes before running and strength training.

Your results will be specific to you. If you are doing this with a running partner, don't be surprised if your specific stretches are different.

Repetitive running creates overuse areas in your musculature. Overused areas or muscles are usually tight. Tightness restricts movement. For running, restricted movement is a negative. Tight muscles also create another issue: a tight muscle inhibits the firing of its opposite muscle, known as 'reciprocal inhibition'. For example, your bicep bends your elbow, while your tricep straightens your elbow. These two muscles have a relationship and if one of them is tight or overused it inhibits the other one. Now let's apply this to your hip area: if your hip flexors are tight, your glutes (buttocks) are inhibited. Your glutes are the biggest, strongest muscle in your body, and one of their jobs is to propel you forward when you run.

Repetitive running tightens your hips, quads and hip flexors. We want our glutes to be firing on all cylinders, and stretching is the way to allow them to function properly. The *Mobility Test* will identify your own specific main areas of tightness that need to be addressed. Please consider these stretches as critical.

Your Mobility Test Equipment:
- ▶ piece of paper
- ▶ cork from a bottle of wine, or similar
- ▶ broom handle

It can be helpful to have someone present while you take the test. Ask them to photograph you as you reach your *maximum hold* position. If there's no-one available, set up your phone on video mode and record the tests. A photographic record will be useful at the end of the six weeks when you retake the test and you can see the improvements achieved by working on your restricted movements.

Mark *Pass* or *Fail* in the table below. It's not unusual to have different results on your right and left side.

	START OF WEEK 3		END OF WEEK 8	
	Left	Right	Left	Right
Calf				
Hamstring				
Quadricep				
Torso Rotator				
Hip Flexor				
Hip Capsule				

1. Calf

Calf Test

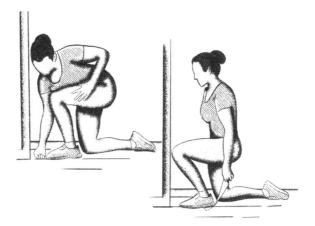

- Facing a wall, kneel on one knee with the opposite foot flat on the floor in front of you.

- Your toes should be 4 inches (10cm or roughly a fist length) from the wall.

- Place a piece of paper under your heel.

- Now that you're in the starting position, attempt to move the knee in front of you to touch the wall.

- Keep your heel on the paper/ground the entire time.

- If you have someone with you, ask them to try and gently pull the paper out from under your heel.

- If you can't touch the wall with your knee, or you need to lift your heel off the paper for your knee to touch the wall, that is a fail.

- Repeat on the other leg.

- Mark your results in the Calf box above. If you fail this test the following stretch is added to your list of exercises.

Calf Stretch

- Place a wedge (e.g. a book) under the front of the foot and repeat the same movement as the test. You should feel the stretch where the calf meets the Achilles tendon.

2. Hamstring

Hamstring Test

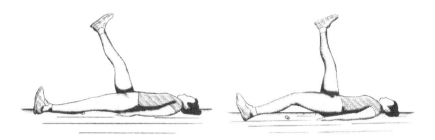

- Lie on your back with your two legs straight out on the ground.

- Place the cork (of a fine wine) on the floor, under the back of one knee.

- Slowly lift the other leg up to a 90-degree angle while keeping it straight.

- If you can't reach 90 degrees, or the leg on the floor lifts from the cork, that is a fail.

- Repeat on the other leg.

- Mark your results in the Hamstring box above. If you fail this test the following stretch is added to your list of exercises.

Hamstring Stretch

- Exactly the same as the test only this time place a resistance band or a towel under your foot and pull.

3. Quadricep

Quadricep Test

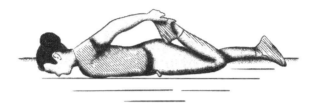

- Lie face down on the floor and place the cork under your left hip.

- Grab your left foot with your left hand, and pull it in to touch your backside.

- If your hip lifts off the cork, or if you cannot touch your backside with your foot, that is a fail.

- Repeat on the other leg.

- Mark your results in the Quadricep box above.

- If you fail this test the stretch is the same as the test.

Quadricep Stretch

- As above.

4. Torso rotators

Torso Rotators Test

- Choose a doorway between two rooms.

- Facing the upright of the frame, sit down, close to
  the doorframe, with your legs crossed at your ankles
  in front of you, like a simple seated yoga pose.

- You should be sitting right in the middle where the two rooms meet,
  the left half of your body in one room, the right half in the other.
  Sitting up nice and straight, place a broom handle across
  your collar bones and hold in place with your two hands.

- Remain in an erect posture and twist your torso with the aim
  of touching the broom off the door frame in front of you.

- Avoid leaning forward to achieve this. Focus on
  rotating only your shoulders, chest and ribcage.

- If you can't touch the stick off the door frame
  without leaning forward, that is a fail.

- Repeat on the other side.

- Mark your results in the Torso Rotators box above. If you fail
  this test the following stretch is added to your exercise list.

Torso Rotators Stretch

- Kneel on your right knee with the opposite foot flat on the floor in front of you. Your right knee should be directly beneath your right hip and your left knee should be at 90 degrees. Hold a broom handle across the back of your shoulders and twist your torso to the left until you feel a stretch. Be sure that your left knee does not move left or right. Repeat on the other side.

5. Hip flexor

Hip Flexor Test

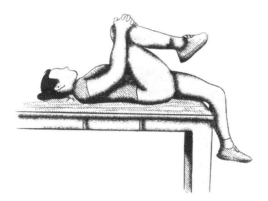

- Lie on your back on a table or some similar surface that will support your body. You want to position yourself so that your head, back and the back of your thighs (hamstrings) are supported by the table while the rest of your legs hang over the side, with the edge of the table about four inches from the crease of your knees.

- Pull one knee to your chest so that any part of your thigh touches your tummy. If the opposite leg lifts off the table in any way, that is a fail.

- Repeat on the other leg. Mark your results in the Hip Flexor box above. If you fail this test the following stretch is added to your exercise list.

Hip Flexor Stretch

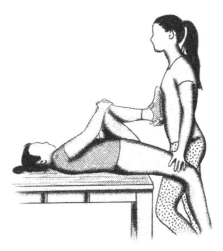

- This a partner-assisted stretch. As with the test, lie on a table with your head, torso and bum supported. For the stretch you want your legs to hang free of the table, feet off the ground. Your partner places one of your feet on their upper chest/shoulder area and moves towards the table, gently driving your knee towards your chest while simultaneously pushing the other knee gently towards the floor.

6. Hip capsule

Hip Capsule Test

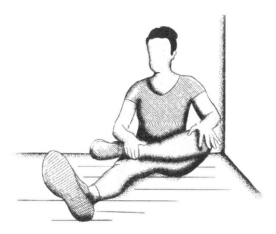

- Sit on the floor in an upright position with your legs straight out in front of you.

- Keeping your right leg straight, put your left ankle just above your right knee. Your legs should make the shape of the number 4.

- Keeping your back straight, you want to try to move your left knee towards the floor. You can use your left hand to add pressure.

- The aim is to get your left thigh parallel to the floor without lifting your right butt cheek or leaning over. If this is not achieved, that is a fail.

- Repeat on the other leg.

- Mark your results in the Hip Capsule box above.

- If you fail this test the stretch is the same as the test.

Hip Capsule Stretch

- As above.

Specific Information on Stretching

If you fail any of the above tests it doesn't mean your life has no meaning and no-one loves you. It simply indicates that those muscles that fail need stretching out over the next six weeks. At the very least this will make you a more fluid runner.

Points to remember:

▶ Stretching is best when you are warm.

▶ Stretches may be uncomfortable but should not be painful.

▶ Hold each stretch for 30 seconds. If you have a situation where one side is much tighter than the other, do three x 30 seconds on the tight side.

▶ Avoid holding your breath.

Your Stretching Programme

Based on the results of your *Mobility Test,* take the corresponding stretching exercises for any you failed and slot these stretches daily into your training programme, ideally when warm. You can find a suggested training plan at the end of this section.

You will continue to include stretching throughout your training season but it will reduce to twice a week once you're in weeks 9–32.

I had been avoiding stretches for 10 years. There is no buzz from it. It is a vital part of the jigsaw puzzle. I suggest, to help you make these stretches a routine, you set aside a specific area in your house with a mat already in place. If you have to start rearranging furniture, you might find yourself reaching to open a bottle of wine instead.

Weeks 3–8: Your Six-Week Integrated Stability Training (IST) Programme

Functional Strength

With two weeks of rest under your belt, and the results from your *Mobility Test* in hand, you're about to embark on a six-week programme. For me, whenever I stop and rest after a long period of training culminating in a race, I get itchy feet. I tend to bounce back pretty quickly and find I am full of energy and ready to get back to training. However, I promise the results from this six-week period will be well worth it.

This training is for *functional* strength. Functional training, like the exercises included here, is designed to help you build strength in the patterns we use in everyday life. The functional programme included here is designed for runners and is called Integrated Stability Training. We are not looking for muscularity *à la* Arnold Schwarzenegger; we are looking for improvement in the organisation and coordination of the muscular system. When you run, your abdominal muscles fire on one side as your opposite leg lands. At least they should. And your glutes fire when your foot hits the ground. At least they should. We have just identified how tight and overused muscles inhibit other muscles. The mobility section deals with the tight muscles. Here we want to strengthen the neural connection between the different muscles that produce force when you run.

Here is an analogy. Your guitar teacher strums the chord of G on her instrument. How many muscular actions have taken place for this to occur? She has straightened and bent her elbow, flicked her wrist and fingers, strummed the strings and already we are at 10 or 12. She taps her foot, arches her shoulder and we are at 20 to 30. She sends one message from her brain and she gets all those numerous movements in one go. I can do all of those movements separately but I can't play G. If I practice them all together, eventually one message from my brain will give me G. This is the goal.

Now compare that to running. When my foot strikes does my glute fire? Do the correct stability muscles in my abdomen fire? Does my back hold my posture straight? Are all the connective supportive muscles firing in one go? We want to practice your leg firing with your glute and your abdominals so they all link into the one message.

This exercise programme rewires you so that the right connections are in place for you to fire what you need to fire together.

There's a saying that repetition is the mother of skill. The technical name is 'engram'. This is a unit of cognitive information inside the brain, the means by which memories are stored as biophysical or biochemical changes in the brain and other neural tissue in response to external stimuli. A little like Daniel in *The Karate Kid*: *wax on, wax off.* When you look at many sports stars, you find that they played a number of sports when young and now they find that so many neural connections are natural.

Functional movement is inhibited by mobility and stability. The target for an endurance runner is to be strong without being big. To have a very efficient running style you need to have good strength in your whole system.

Remember that the muscles that stabilise you when you are running also maintain your posture. Therefore it is important to hold good posture when doing the following exercises. During all the exercises, tuck and squeeze your abdominal muscles.

Integrated Stability Training Programme (IST)

CORE CIRCUIT

Complete three circuits of these four core-conditioning exercises

1. Elbow plank with leg raise

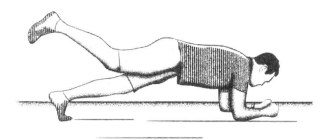

The focus point here is the abdominal muscles. Get into an elbow plank position. Tuck and flex the abdominal muscles to hold the stable position of your lower back. Do 8 leg raises with each leg, building to 12 repetitions.

2. Floor bridge

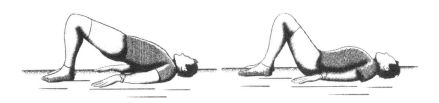

Lie on your back, knees bent and feet near your bum. Before lifting your hips up, squeeze your abdominal muscles and both buttocks. Lift your hips, hold up for five seconds maintaining the squeeze, and lower. Begin with 8 repetitions, building to 12.

3. V-Sit with rotation

Hold a weight (3–5kg) with both hands, close to your chest. Sit with feet together, back straight, lean slightly back, and raise your heels off the floor. Rotate at a steady pace, keeping your eyes on your hands. Reach alternately to each side and touch the floor. Begin with 8 repetitions, building to 12.

4. Hop

Stand on one leg, jump up and forward and land on the same leg. Land as steady as you can with a bent leg and good posture. Begin with 8 repetitions on each leg, building to 12.

FUNCTIONAL EXERCISES CIRCUIT

Complete the next four functional exercises A to D using the following guidelines.

- ▶ In your first session complete 3 sets of eight repetitions of each exercise on each side with 60 seconds rest in between sets.
- ▶ In your second session do the very same except complete three sets of nine repetitions.
- ▶ Increase the repetitions of each set of each exercise by one every session until you reach 12 repetitions, then increase the weight by 1 or 2kg and start back again at eight repetitions.

A. Lunge to balance with one arm overhead press

Stand tall and strong, maintain tucked and squeezed abdominals. Hold the weight, by your side, in your right hand and step your right foot back into a lunge. Keep steady. Stand up and, without putting your right foot down, raise your right knee to hip height as you simultaneously raise the weight over your head. Suggested weight 3–6kg. Begin with 8 repetitions, building to 12. Repeat on left side.

B. Single-leg, one-arm, bent-over row

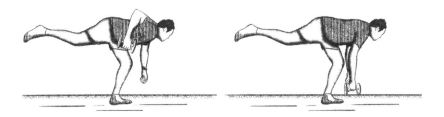

Raising one leg behind you, lean forward and try to get your back into a horizontal position. Take weight in the same hand as the leg you have raised. Bring elbow up to ribcage, pause and lower again. Supporting leg stays slightly bent, keep back straight and shoulders tucked back. Keep steady. Suggested weight 5–10kg. Begin with 8 repetitions, building to 12. Repeat on other side.

C. Single leg squat

Place an average kitchen chair or a bench of similar height 4 inches (10cm) behind your heels. Lift one foot off the ground. Keeping that foot off the ground, slowly move into a sitting position and aim to touch your backside gently off the edge of the chair. Reach your arms forward to stop yourself falling backwards. Still keeping that foot raised, move back into a standing position. Keep steady. No weight needed. Keep foot off the ground for the duration. Begin with 8 repetitions, building to 12. Repeat on the other leg.

D. Single-leg, one-arm lateral raise

Stand upright and lift your left leg a few inches off the floor. Put the weight in your left hand and, keeping your arm straight, lift to the side from your thigh to shoulder height and back down. Be careful not to lean towards either side. Keep steady. Suggested weight 2–5kg. Begin with 8 repetitions, building to 12. Repeat on right side.

Weeks 3–8: Suggested IST Plan

So let's take stock. We have had two weeks of rest and we are entering into a six-week block of pre-season training. We want to lower the volume of running considerably to rest any overused areas. However, we don't want to stop running altogether as we want to maintain elasticity in the tendons and preserve a certain level of aerobic activity. We want to stretch any tight areas as identified by the *Mobility Test,* and we want to reorchestrate how our muscles synchronise themselves while running using the *IST.* So, how do we fit all this effectively into a weekly plan?

We want to run three times per week and we want to do our *IST* three times per week. We also want to stretch. My suggestion is to stretch a minimum of once a day for your specific stretches, but twice a day is better. All the stretches should also be done after every run. If you have time to do more of one thing, make it stretching.

Week	Mon	Tues	Wed
1	Rest	Rest	Rest
2	Rest	Rest	Rest
3	Take your *Mobility Test*	Stretch	**3 miles** followed by IST Circuits + Stretches
4	Stretch	Stretch	**3 miles** followed by IST Circuits + Stretches
5	Stretch	Stretch	**3 miles** followed by IST Circuits + Stretches
6	Stretch	Stretch	**3 miles** followed by IST Circuits + Stretches
7	Stretch	Stretch	**3 miles** followed by IST Circuits + Stretches
8	Stretch	Stretch	**3 miles** followed by IST Circuits + Stretches

Thur	Fri	Sat	Sun
Rest	Rest	Rest	Rest
Rest	Rest	Rest	Rest
Stretch	**3 miles** followed by IST Circuits + Stretches	Stretch	**3 miles** followed by IST Circuits + Stretches
Stretch	**3 miles** followed by IST Circuits + Stretches	Stretch	**5 miles** followed by IST Circuits + Stretches
Stretch	**3 miles** followed by IST Circuits + Stretches	Stretch	**7 miles** followed by IST Circuits + Stretches
Stretch	**3 miles** followed by IST Circuits + Stretches	Stretch	**9 miles** followed by IST Circuits + Stretches
Stretch	**3 miles** followed by IST Circuits + Stretches	Stretch	**10 miles** followed by IST Circuits + Stretches
Stretch	**3 miles** followed by IST Circuits + Stretches	Stretch	**11 miles** followed by IST Circuits + Stretches Finally, repeat your *Mobility Test*

With your long runs now up to 11 miles, you are perfectly placed to start your 24-week training plan.

Weeks 9–32: The Peak Performance Chart and Training Plan

If you have ever finished a race and fallen short of your target, you'll know that it feels pretty rough. And if the reason is that you didn't have the discipline to do what it takes to prepare properly, it can leave you feeling very low. It stinks and it lingers – I know, I have felt it.

To give yourself the best chance of fulfilling your true potential in a race, choose from either the *Minimum Training Plan* for your first 100-miler, or the *Advanced Training Plan*. Alongside your running training, you're going to be disciplined in a number of areas, all of which are covered in detail and programmed in the *Peak Performance Chart*.

The *Peak Performance Chart* shows how small gains are turned into large gains. In an endurance race small improvements in efficiency can make a huge difference over all those miles. Improvements never come in big chunks; they come in seemingly insignificant pennies. If you see a penny on the ground, would you bother picking it up? Pick up pennies wherever you can. All together they will make the difference.

The *Peak Performance Chart* uses a scoring system and is designed to make it clear at a glance how your preparation is going. There are 20 sections on the chart, yet you will notice that only five involve running. This is to give you a complete body and mind training over the 24 weeks leading up to the race, with 20 activities all working to get you ready for one event. Each activity carries a weighted score and, if everything is completed, a total score of 100 can be achieved weekly.

You will track and complete your scores on the *Peak Performance Chart* each week. The closer you get to 100 each week, the stronger and more prepared you are and the better chance you will have of finishing the race and performing to your ability.

How to complete your Peak Performance Chart

When I ran my first 100-mile ultra I only ran. I did spend the following three days on crutches, but I finished. Slowly, as my training improved and my experience grew with each race, the *Peak Performance Chart* was developed. The idea of charting and analysing the results of your 24 weeks of preparation is to allow you to see how you are doing at a glance. You will always be on top of your own progress, in control of your preparations and building your confidence.

Follow the guidelines below as to how to rate your performance each week. The completed chart below shows 100%, a 'perfect' score, but if you can aim to stay over 80% consistently, you will be in good shape and well prepared for your race. If you're finding it hard to get to 80% each week, don't worry, and don't be too hard on yourself.

Each of the 20 focus areas are explained in detail in the next section.

In the Appendices you will find 24 blank *Peak Performance Charts* prefilled with the 20 areas of focus which you can fill out each week.

Sample Completed Weekly Peak Performance Chart

WEEKLY PEAK PERFORMANCE CHART

		M	T	W	T	F	S	S	TOTAL
Stretching	2 x 2 points	2			2				4/4
Recovery Run	1 x 2 points	2							2/2
Hill Run / Fartlek Run	1 x 5 points			5					5/5
Regular Run	2 x 1 points				1			1	2/2
Long Run	1 x 5 points						5		5/5
Alternative Exercise	1 x 2 points		2						2/2
Rest & Recovery	2 x 3 points	3				3			6/6
Sleep	7 x 1 points	1	1	1	1	1	1	1	7/7
Education	3 x 1 points			1			1	1	3/3
Food Planning	1 x 2 points						2		2/2
Food Shopping	1 x 2 points						2		2/2
Food Preparation	7 x 1 points	1	1	1	1	1	1	1	7/7
Eating	7 x 2 points	2	2	2	2	2	2	2	14/14
IST & Maintaining Pre-Season	1 x 4 points				4				4/4
Mental Resilience	7 x 1 points	1	1	1	1	1	1	1	7/7
Visualisation	2 x 1 points	1					1		2/2
Self-talk	1 x 5 points						5		5/5
Hydration	7 x 1 points	1	1	1	1	1	1	1	7/7
Discipline & Consistency	7 x 1 points	1	1	1	1	1	1	1	7/7
Laughter	7 x 1 points	1	1	1	1	1	1	1	7/7

TOTAL 100/100

Sample: Completed Weekly Peak Performance Chart

The 20 Focus Areas of the Peak Performance Chart

Stretching

Take your *Stretching Programme* from weeks 3–8 and include it twice a week going forward. You can repeat the mobility tests to track your progress and adjust the stretches, as required.

Score yourself 2 points for each completed stretching session
Max: 4 points weekly

Recovery Run

A recovery run is a short, slow run (shorter than your base sessions, and at a pace slower than your average run), completed within 24 hours of a hard session such as an interval workout or a long run. An easy run clears lactic acid that may have been produced on the long run.

Seasoned runners need easy days in order to maintain hard-earned aerobic fitness and make continual gains in running economy. Runners with good economy use less oxygen than runners with poor economy at the same speed. Running economy has also been shown to be a useful predictor of endurance-running performance. Recovery runs initiate the process of muscle repair. Running increases the blood flow to your muscles, but at a pace gentle enough to avoid additional muscle damage. Your muscles will contract and tighten if you do nothing but sit on the couch the whole day. You can also use your recovery runs to help you work on improving the way you run and your biomechanics. Pay attention to your technique and don't worry about anything else. These easy runs are at your own easy pace, not your friend's easy pace. There is no such thing as going too slowly on these days as long as you are running.

Running at slower paces also promotes fat burning, as your body can only burn fat by running at a slower pace. To burn fat effectively, your body needs oxygen. To ensure you are getting enough oxygen, you need to be running at a low enough intensity where you can comfortably hold a conversation without being out of breath. By slowing down, your body will get better at generating energy from fat and, over time, you'll be able to run faster (and burn more calories) while maintaining the percentage of energy coming from fat.

This is often the most enjoyable run of the week for me. I have no pressure to go any distance or speed. I nearly always arrive home feeling better than before I left.

Score yourself 2 points for completing a recovery run
Max: 2 points weekly

Hill Runs

Until a few years ago I always avoided hills. Hills are hard work. When training for the Düsseldorf Marathon in 2016, my regular training partner Emma and I decided to make this the best marathon we could and from that moment on neither of us backed down or missed a training session. As part of our mid-week schedule we ran a warm-up route that finished at the bottom of a reasonably long (about 500m), steep hill. The first night we arrived at the bottom of the hill in lashing rain. We knew why we were there, so we just said encouraging things like, *Okay, let's do this*. We sprinted about 370 metres and slowly ran back down while catching our breath, then we gave it one minute and went again. We repeated it three times before heading back to base.

Four weeks later we were sprinting the full 500 metres with five or six repeats. The key to maintaining our progress was to monitor recovery time. After each sprint we would slowly jog to the starting position at the base of the hill, wait 60 seconds and go again. If we hadn't recovered in that time we would skip the next hill sprint. As the weeks went by, we found that the recovery time shortened. I noticed the difference within a few weeks: I lost a kilo and felt stronger and a lot fitter. Since then, I like hills a bit more.

Uphill sprinting builds muscular endurance and muscle strength because the major muscles of the body must work harder to propel your body up a hill. The slope of a hill targets the glutes, hamstrings, quadriceps, calves, core and upper body.

Along with leg-muscle strength, training on hills quickens your stride, expands stride length, develops your cardiovascular system, enhances your running economy and can even protect your leg muscles against soreness. In short, hill running will make you a stronger, faster and healthier runner. What's more, the benefits are relatively quick to take effect. In as little as a few weeks of regular hill training you can expect a significant improvement in your muscle power and speed. Hills strengthen tendons and ligaments, reduce the risk of injury and improve overall running form.

Hill intervals are the most basic and yet one of the most beneficial of all running sessions. Like walking, running is a concentric movement, meaning the muscles in use shorten as they contract. It's a deliberate and controlled action using the calves, glutes, hamstrings and quads. All these muscles fire repeatedly when we run uphill, which is why it doesn't take much time to raise your heart rate. Your lungs and heart will reap the benefits as your cardiovascular system becomes stronger.

Hill running and fartlek runs increase your anaerobic threshold, meaning the speed you can comfortably run at over a long period of time goes up. Hill runs are the key to endurance, but 2020 was the first year that I put them into practice properly. Before I had done hill sprints once a week, but from 2020 I included long hill climbs in all my long runs. Knowing that the Connemara 100 was looming large at the end of the summer, for six weeks in a row I made the weekly long run a mountain run. The result was clear to me when I ran the last 20 miles of the Connemara 100 feeling reasonably okay.

Running hills comes with a health warning, however. Approach with caution, make sure you are fit and start slowly. My wife Fiona was recently getting back into running after a few years out and started training for a marathon. Slowly she increased her runs for the first five weeks.

By week six it was hard to hold her back. We ran to the local village which has a steep 300-metre hill and did five hill sprints followed by a slow run home. Within sight of our house I saw her slightly stumble. Her calf muscle had torn, which meant she would be out for four or five weeks. The pain of not being able to run, just as it seemed to be coming together, was far greater than the pain of the tear.

Score yourself 5 points for completing a hill run
Max: 5 points weekly*

*You will be alternating hill and fartlek runs, weekly.

Fartlek Runs

Fartlek runs challenge the body to adapt to various speeds, conditioning you to become faster over longer distances. Incorporating these surges of speed helps runners to gauge and learn how much they can push their bodies over shorter segments while at the same time keeping enough physical and mental energy in reserve to go the whole distance and complete a race.

Fartleks, a type of interval training, are an ideal workout for almost all runners because of the variety of physical benefits they offer. They'll make you stronger, faster and more efficient. Both fartlek and interval training improve $\dot{V}O_2$ max, which is our maximum rate of oxygen consumption. The higher one's $\dot{V}O_2$ max, the greater one's ability to efficiently utilise oxygen to power the muscles and maintain performance. Also, both types of training increase lactate threshold, the level at which lactate starts to enter the blood. When you get muscle cramps you can thank lactic acid. If you increase the threshold at which lactate starts to build up, you can decrease cramps and increase performance.

Thirdly, both types of training increase ventilatory threshold, the point at which breathing rate starts to increase, eventually to the point where breathing becomes laboured and challenging. Basically, you can delay the point at which you become breathless when you're running with some good speed work.

How does it work? Once you're nice and warm, about 15 minutes or a mile into your run, you can start your fartlek work simply by picking up the pace for a short distance, say running to the traffic lights or to the big tree on the far side of the park. Once you reach the target, revert to your regular pace for a couple of minutes before going again. If it is difficult returning to regular pace after each fast minute, you are running the surge too fast. To improve your endurance, reduce the recovery segments.

Score yourself 5 points for completing a fartlek run
Max: 5 points weekly*

*You will be alternating fartlek and hill runs, weekly.

Regular Runs

The purpose of regular runs is to spend time on your feet. You don't want to be sprinting or putting yourself through anything particularly difficult. Apart from adding miles, you are building discipline and consistency.

Score yourself 1 point for completing each of your regular runs
Max: 2 points weekly

Long Runs

Continuous long runs help build resilience and mental toughness. The long run is the most specific for mental and physical preparation. It improves your running form. Muscles learn through practice and your stride will improve through consistent long runs and you will increase the efficiency of fuel use. Running for prolonged periods increases the strength of your leg muscles and connective tissues, but also those of the respiratory system (including the diaphragm and core region).

With every long run you are tasting a bit of race day. This is your time to check everything out. Your clothing and footwear, your food and water intake. If you prefer music, audiobooks, podcasts or listening to the world go by. How you deal with exhaustion and boredom. How you react when something goes wrong, like your food somehow forgot to put itself in your backpack. How you react to a fall or getting caught in a hailstorm. Earlier this year, on a long run, I stopped for a drink and realised that I had none. It was hot and I was sweating and thirsty and it was nine miles to the next shop. By the time I got there I was weak, but I lived. This is your best chance to mimic race day.

Overly long runs can take too much recovery time – e.g. a 50-mile run when training for a 100-mile race. Instead it can be useful to run back-to-backs, e.g. a 30-mile run followed by a 25-mile run the following day. It is good to force yourself out in a tired body on tired legs. On a long run I often loop by the house every five to 10 miles for food. It saves having to carry too many supplies. If you know the profile of your race, you can try to mimic it on these long runs.

Score yourself 5 points for completing your long run
Max: 5 points weekly

Alternative Exercise (Cross-Training)

The idea is to be active but to have a break from running so you can stretch and move different muscles. Cross-training is any sport or exercise that supplements your main sport.

Studies show that cross-training offers many benefits for runners. It helps balance your muscle groups. It can help to strengthen muscles that are used less during running. You can focus on specific areas, such as your upper body, that don't get worked as much while running. By balancing your weaker muscles with your stronger ones, you'll help reduce your chance of injury. Participating in low-impact cross-training activities such as swimming will reduce the stress on your joints. Many cross-training activities are great cardiovascular workouts.

I like to swim, hill walk or do a gym session focussed on upper-body strength and mobility. An ideal week for me would be a slow, short recovery run on a Monday along with my stretches. Tuesday one hour doing lengths in the pool. Wednesday hill sprints or fartlek. The Thursday run to get in some miles followed by stretches and my *IST Programme*. Friday off. Saturday long run. Sunday second weekend run, long but shorter than Saturday's.

Score yourself 2 points for completing a cross-training session
Max: 2 points weekly

Rest and Recovery

Rest can sometimes mean recovery but it always means rest. During a training season, rest days are essential. A successful fitness plan isn't complete without rest days. Taking regular breaks allows your body to recover, repair and strengthen. It's a critical part of your progress, regardless of your fitness level or sport. This is the time that the body adapts to the stress of exercise and the real training effect takes place. Rest is necessary for avoiding exercise-induced fatigue.

Exercise depletes your muscles' glycogen levels. If these stores aren't replenished through adequate food and rest, you'll experience muscle fatigue and soreness. Plus, your muscles need glycogen to function, even when you're not running. Without sufficient time to repair and replenish, the body will continue to break down from intensive exercise. It can be difficult to get enough rest into a training schedule, especially within a few weeks of a race date. However, just like the long runs, this is something you cannot skip or overlook. This is where you grow.

Understanding that this is a major part of the plan is essential. Sometimes it feels wrong to have a lazy day and it goes against everything you are training yourself to do. Relax and go with it!

We're looking to schedule as much rest as possible each week. As there are five days of running in the programme, along with an alternative training day, and only seven days in a week, you only have one true rest day. Try to go easy on the day of your short recovery run when you also do a stretching session to add some additional rest into your week. Typically this falls on a Monday, as most people schedule their long runs over the weekend.

Score yourself 3 points for each rest day
Max: 6 points weekly

Sleep

Sleep is essential for the body to function at any level, let alone as a well-tuned machine. Sleep is vital for your health and well-being. When you're sleeping your body continues to work, both supporting how your brain functions and maintaining your physical condition. Regular good sleep keeps your memory sharp, gives you energy, boosts creativity and focuses your attention.

According to Dr Nerina Ramlakhan, a sleep expert and author of *Tired But Wired: How to Overcome Your Sleep Problems: The Essential Sleep Toolkit*, the sleep that occurs before the clock strikes midnight is one of the most powerful phases we can get, because it's the period where the body is replenished.

She explains that there is a synchronicity to the movements of the moon and the cells in our body. *As the light level drops below a certain limit, it sends a message to the pineal gland through the eyes, and then every cell in the body starts adjusting its functions.* Sleep problems include having a difficult time falling asleep, struggling to stay asleep, waking up several times during the sleep cycle or waking up too early and being unable to go back to sleep.

Our immune system relies on sleep to stay strong. Ongoing sleep deficiency can mean you'll struggle to fight infections and will be more susceptible to colds and flu. When your body gets the sleep it needs, your immune cells and proteins get the rest they need to fight off whatever comes their way.

A good night's sleep also helps prevent weight gain. It is extremely difficult to fight junk food cravings when you are low on energy and sleep. Lack of sleep can cause your body to release cortisol, a stress hormone that triggers your heart to work harder. Regular good sleep helps reduce stress and improve your memory. It can lower your blood pressure, keep your heart healthy and give more clarity to your brain. When you get to the business end of training, going to bed early is key.

Anyone who works shift work or nights will be familiar with the term 'the graveyard shift'. It is aptly named, as you can end up like the walking dead. In 2007 the World Health Organisation classified night shift work as a probable carcinogen due to circadian disruption. Our bodies are programmed to run on cycles known as circadian rhythms, from the Latin meaning 'around' or 'approximately' (circa) 'a day' (diem). The circadian rhythm, the name given to your body's 24-hour internal clock, controls your body's sleep-wake cycle, and changes in your routine disrupt those rhythms. There are other influencers of your body's internal clock, including melatonin (a hormone released in your brain that plays a role in sleep), physical activity and social behaviours. Your age can also influence your sensitivity to the sleep-wake cycle.

In training for the Connemara 100, I set the alarm for 2 a.m. and 3 a.m. on a few occasions, got up and ran. It's one thing to break out of a good night's sleep and get up and go for a run. But to do it the night after a long 31-mile run when you are dog-tired and in the deepest sleep is extremely difficult. If you do have the strength to get out of bed, that level of discomfort is close to resembling parts of a 100-miler.

The night before my first 50km race I was so nervous I only slept one hour, from 10 p.m. to 11 p.m. I was worried sick that my day was ruined before it had started. Luckily, I was wrong. A poor night's sleep before a race does not always hurt your performance. Pre-race nerves contribute to performance, so there is no need to get over-anxious or stressed over not sleeping well the night before. Getting quality sleep in the days prior to that is what is most important for performance.

My bedtime routine includes taking a magnesium supplement and getting to bed by 10 p.m. Not only does magnesium promote sleep, it's also excellent for muscle recovery after exercise and is essential for calcium absorption. I take *Mag365 Bone Formula* in powder form about an hour before bed. You dissolve a teaspoon in some hot (not boiling) water. This process converts it to ionic magnesium citrate, one of the most bioavailable forms to take. It combines magnesium citrate with calcium and vitamins C, D3 and K2, together with boron, all essential for bone health. After that all the screens get switched off. I switch my phone to airplane mode and charge it downstairs. Decide on the bedtime routine that would best suit your life and try to stick to it.

Score yourself 1 point for every night you follow your bedtime routine
Max: 7 points weekly

Education

No matter the level we're starting from, education is something that benefits us all. Take 45 minutes two or three times a week for listening, watching or reading something on improving your ultra-running.

To get a better understanding of the workings of the athlete's mind, I went back to college and studied sport psychology. For me it was fascinating. I saw this as an opportunity to get one step closer to psychologically stepping up to an event like a 100-mile ultra. It was inspiring to listen to guest lecturers, former athletes, talk about how they coped in times of stress. What I learned was that anyone can become mentally strong. It just takes awareness and practice.

Not everyone has the desire or opportunity to go to college but if you spend 45 minutes two or three times a week listening to, watching or reading material related to your goal, you will be propelled in that direction. Focus is powerful. If you are focused on cultivating good habits, your energy will make things happen. To control your time, you will have to prioritise your tasks and delegate them, defer them or do them. To read that book or watch that documentary you will have to dump the distractions.

When training for a race I live it. I focus on the journey. On long runs I listen to audiobooks; more often than not, it's someone with more experience than me talking about how they prepared for, coped with and raced such an event. During rest evenings I sneak documentaries on the same subject if I'm alone. I'm constantly reading about nutritional ideas and recipes. I'm always looking for something that I didn't know. I usually find it. It's never-ending but never dull.

Michael Greger MD's *How Not to Die* lists the 15 most common causes of death in the US then tells you how to avoid them by what you eat. It would take me a lifetime to research and decipher so much information yet here I have it all in one book. I enjoyed reading it so much that I bought the audiobook too so I could listen to Michael Gregor read it to me himself. T. Colin Campbell and his son Thomas M. Campbell, now a physician, shared findings with the world in *The China Study*, hailed as one of the most important books about diet and health ever written.

Adharanand Finn spent six months in Kenya and wrote, *Running with the Kenyans*. From reading this I got months of experience and knowledge that I never had to leave my sofa for. Christopher McDougall spent months in Mexico hanging out with the mysterious Tarahumara Mexican Indians researching *Born to Run*, observing their lifestyle to find out what makes them reputedly the best ultra-runners in the world. In July 2015, ultramarathon legend Scott Jurek smashed the world record for running the sprawling 2,189-mile Appalachian Trail that extends nearly the entire length of the United States. His book *North* shares that journey.

In the 11 years that I have been running, I've read hundreds of books on running, diet, psychology and feats of human endeavour. I'm so grateful for the effort behind each and every book, the people who spend months and even years finding out the hows and the whys and the wherefores and then share their experience freely with passion and expertise. After every non-fiction book I read I come away a little bit wiser. The more knowledge you can absorb, the better and more inspired and ready you will be.

Score yourself 1 point for each educational session you complete
Max: 3 points weekly

Food Planning

Taking responsibility for what we eat has a huge impact on our health. You might want to eat a healthy meal on Tuesday but it's not going to happen if you arrive home and have nothing healthy to cook because you hadn't time to shop.

For me this has to start with a plan. Come the weekend I will pick out two or three main meals for the following week and check the recipes against what we have in our cupboards. Because we regularly eat a lot of the same meals, we don't have to go out and buy everything each time we make it. Usually all we need are the fresh ingredients, as the herbs, spices and often the dry ingredients are in the cupboard. You'll find the recipes mentioned here in the appendix at the end.

A typical week might look like this:

Breakfast: Monday to Friday we usually have a slice of toast with peanut butter and banana or hummus and pesto. Breakfast is quick as I start work early.

11 a.m. snack: green vegetable smoothie or fresh fruit salad or overnight oats, all prepared the night before.

Lunch: we try to make enough dinner so that there is at least enough for lunch the next day for both of us, or enough to freeze for another day, later in the week.

Dinner: Fiona loves trying out the vegan versions of typical meat dishes. Our regular meals include: vegan sushi with avocado, cucumber, spring onions, red pepper and carrot; lentil shepherd-less pie; pad thai with tofu and vegetables; stir-fry vegetables with brown rice; baked potatoes or sweet potatoes with an everything salad[1].

We'll also often have a big pot of soup and a loaf of homemade bread when we feel like something lighter. If you're looking for a great bread recipe to try, I'd recommend looking up *My New Roots, Life-Changing Loaf of Bread*. It's packed full of oats, seeds, nuts and is gluten and dairy free.

At the weekend, with a little more time to prepare food, we usually have a cooked breakfast, often marinated tofu with mushrooms, onions, garlic and greens served with leftover potato (made into potato cakes) or a potato rösti. The weekend is also when we are most likely to treat ourselves to a takeaway from our local Indian or Thai restaurants on one of the nights.

Without planning, the whole week's healthy eating collapses before it even begins. There have been times when we've been too lazy or have been away for the weekend and the weekly planning and shopping haven't

---

1   The 'everything' salad should really be called the 'whatever' salad because we add whatever salad ingredients we have in the fridge.

happened. Those weeks are always bad food weeks. It's also more expensive. Good healthy food makes me feel strong and energised; the opposite makes me feel poorly.

Score yourself 2 points for planning your food for the week
Max: 2 points weekly

Food Shopping

Get up, get out and buy the ingredients. This can take time when you are a coeliac vegan. At the weekend I usually go to the organic market, the regular supermarket and the health food shop. I try to stick to the list we have written based on what is required for the week ahead. It sounds simple, but when I'm standing in *Nurney Farm Organics*, or *Christie's Organic Fruit & Veg*, looking at all the gorgeous produce, it can be very hard to resist buying everything in sight.

Good things to have in stock for the week are:

Vegetables: broccoli, cauliflower, courgettes, cucumbers, celery, fennel, avocados, kale and/or spinach, salad leaves (e.g. rocket), carrots, beetroot, sweet potatoes, onions, spring onions, peppers, fresh sweetcorn.

Fruit: blueberries, mango, melon, pomegranate, bananas, lemons, limes and oranges.

I do not want to spend my last few years on this planet suffering and sick if I can avoid it. I want to feel alive and good until I die. Is that too much to ask for? I don't think so (and neither does Michael Greger MD, author of *How Not to Die*). From what I've learnt, the best chance we can give ourselves is to eat well and exercise, regardless of what my parents and grandparents did, or what others around me do.

Score yourself 2 points for doing your weekly food shop
Max: 2 points weekly

Food Preparation

Turning all that gorgeous fresh produce into the meals you have planned takes effort. Whether you enjoy making that effort or not will probably impact upon how often you choose to cook each week. Typically we cook about four times a week and, as I said, try to make four to six portions so that we have enough for that meal, lunch or dinner the next day and maybe a couple of portions that can go in the freezer. Fiona and I are lucky in that we eat the same meals and share the workload. I know that not everybody is in the same boat and some families have to cater for different diets and tastes at each meal, adding to the effort required.

Although the cooking can be reduced to three or four times a week (if that's your preference), there are a few tasks that tend to happen every evening after work in our house: the making of smoothies or fruit salad or overnight oats.

We both drink green smoothies most days and we have a stash of glass bottles that we reuse. Ideally you make these fresh, for immediate consumption, but we have found that making them the night before works best for us. This is food prep that needs to happen each day. I've included a general recipe at the end of the book.

On work days I bring overnight oats or fruit salad for my morning break.

Overnight oats are simple and, as the name suggests, can be prepared the night before. Take a container that holds about the same as a cereal bowl. Fill roughly a third with porridge oats, a third with toppings you like (e.g. fresh berries, sliced banana, grated apple, dried fruit, chopped nuts, seeds, cinnamon, cacao nibs – the list is endless) and cover with your preferred liquid. I use rice milk or water.

For my fruit salad I usually go for a mix of mango, pineapple, melon, blueberries and pomegranate. If all I have is melon, that will do. I top it with a mix of seeds and sometimes unsweetened coconut yogurt. Not bothering to prep either oats or fruit makes for a pretty miserable morning break at work. I really do thrive on eating well.

If you like to have a sweet treat, the best route you can take is to make something yourself. Of course, there are a lot of bars out there, particularly those marketed at active people, and more and more I see snacks that are vegan, gluten-free and sugar-free. However, a lot of packaged goods contain more sugar and more added fats than if you make them yourself. I have included a recipe for my favourite sweet treat in the recipe section. A raw, vegan raspberry and vanilla cheesecake.

For speed, you can't beat eating a piece of fruit. Bananas, known as nature's power bar, are packed with carbohydrates and potassium, which supports nerve and muscle function. Carbs are fuel for our body and brain, and they account for 90% of banana calories. I tend to go for no-cook, quick and easy savoury snacks: slices of apple with peanut butter; corn cakes or rice cakes with hummus or peanut butter; toasted sandwich with avocado, hummus, sprouts, pesto.

Lunches are probably my most important meal as my time is limited at work. I tend to eat my main meal at lunchtime. I often run in the evening straight after work so I rely on lunch to fuel me and make me feel strong. The better I eat at lunch, the better I am likely to feel by the following weekend. I've included recipes for all my favourite main meals in the section at the end of the book.

My evening meal tends to be something simple like soup and brown bread or brown pasta with pesto stirred through. I find these easier to digest and tend to sleep better when I eat lighter food last thing at night.

Finally, I suggest that you also start to prepare specific food for your weekly long run(s). Race day is not the time to find out that *Scotch eggs* don't agree with you. (I'm not sure who thought that a cooked egg, surrounded by a layer of sausage meat, coated in breadcrumbs and then deep fried, was the food of champions, but I have been offered them on two separate occasions in the middle of a race, so I'm guessing they work for some runners.) Use your long runs to try out a variety of foods to see how they work while you run.

On the morning of a long run I eat porridge early. Very early. Typically, if I am going to run at 8 a.m., I get up at 6 a.m. to eat porridge and hop back into bed. It gives my body time to start digesting the oats and slow-releasing those carbs that will fuel the miles. As my route often uses my house as a feeding station, I practice eating on the run. After a lot of trial and error, mostly on race days, I made a conscious decision that during my training for the Connemara 100 race I would eat during all of my long runs and figure it out once and for all.

Figuring out what works best for you will stand to you on race day. You're aiming to consume somewhere between 200 and 350 calories an hour. Your body won't tolerate much more than that over a long period of time as you bounce up and down. What form those calories take is key. Only practice will determine what works best for you. Unfortunately, you'll be burning a lot more than that, anything from 400 to 600 calories per hour depending on a number of factors including your metabolism and the pace you are running at. So, yes, you will have a calorie deficit by the end of the race but you can help to keep 'bonking' at bay by topping up your calories from early in the run with foods that sustain you.

In Phil Maffetone's *The Big Book of Endurance Training and Racing* I learnt about how you can use heart-rate training to help burn fat so that you are not solely reliant on carbohydrates when you run. If your interest in endurance running is focused on your health, as mine is, I would recommend picking up a copy of his book. A lot of ultra-runners fuel themselves, almost exclusively, on sports drinks, gels and bars. I tried that for a while in the early days but they didn't agree with me. When I found that I could eat whole foods, nutritious homemade snacks like soup or dolmades, and run without an upset stomach, I chose that route. Find what works for you and test it over the coming weeks.

Score yourself 1 point for preparing your food for the day ahead
Max: 7 points weekly

Eating

Buying the food and making the meals is all great. But you have to actually eat it. It's a bit like press-ups; no-one can do them for you.

There's nothing more disheartening than finding your salad and vegetables rotting at the back of the fridge. Of course, there will be weeks when unexpected invitations to lunch or dinner appear after the goods have been bought, but if that's happening regularly, you'll end up wasting time and money planning and shopping and you won't necessarily be eating well enough.

Like all the other focus areas in the *Peak Performance Chart*, we are looking to get you to the start line, and many hours later the finish line, of your first ultramarathon in good shape. What you eat to get you there will have a material impact on that quest.

You are what you eat and, speaking as someone who used to celebrate crossing the finish line of a race with a steak and a bottle of red wine (actually I used to celebrate everything with a steak and a bottle of red wine), I'm glad that I changed what I was eating. Only good things will come from putting your focus on what you will eat over the 32 weeks of this programme. It will impact how you feel when you run and how well you recover after each session. The food you choose to eat may well be different to what I outline in these pages, but try to make it a conscious choice with a focus on your goal. Although the idea of 'good food' is subjective, you'll know it when you eat it.

Score yourself 2 points each time you have a 'good food' day
Max: 14 points weekly

IST and Maintaining the Pre-Season Benefits

Poor alignment is the reason we programmed six weeks to focus on your functional movement before introducing running into the plan. The way to maintain the pre-season benefits is to continue your *IST Programme* once a week.

To keep yourself in good shape for the 24 weeks of training culminating in the 100-miler will take some work. Mentally and physically you are going to have to work hard, rest hard and be very aware of your health, staying free of injury. As far as your body is concerned, this is an 'overuse adventure' in the sense that all of your muscles will consistently be overused. If your body were a car, obviously it would need maintenance along with several top-ups of petrol and oil to make sure it didn't splutter and stop. Similarly, you will need to keep your eye on your general health and energy levels. This requires attention to overtraining, nutrition and running technique.

It seems logical to think that if I run more or faster in training then I will improve. But remember that the progressions are built into a good training plan. Don't just think, *Well, I'll do more and that will put me further ahead*. It doesn't always work that way; often that's overtraining. Trust your training plan.

When training for an ultra, it's easy to get an injury. Overtraining is the biggest cause of injuries and poor performance. Poor nutrition is also a major factor in causing injury. For a lot of runners injury is a part of life and has to be dealt with. The most common injuries for runners are runner's knee, Achilles tendonitis, IT band syndrome, shin splints, hamstring injuries, plantar fasciitis, stress fractures and ankle sprains. As you can see, they are all in the knees, legs and feet. They all make for dull reading, unless you are suffering from one. I have elaborated on each in the running injuries section at the back of the book.

So how do you alleviate the effects of overuse? The obvious answer is rest and recovery. Rest is straightforward – take your rest days, go to bed early and don't engage in other strenuous activities. Recovery has more to it and can include many things such as nutrition, hydration, massage, stretching, low-impact recovery activities like yoga, time with friends and family, reading, meditation or spending time on hobbies.

Poor running technique is a seldom-considered area of this whole process. It is, however, an important one. To go back to the car analogy: if the tracking on the wheels of your car is not straight, the result is that one side of your tyre looks brand new and the other side is worn bare. This is similar to how an injury occurs. If your body is not aligned correctly, you get more pressure on one side of a joint than the other and this becomes inflamed and painful.

So how does your body develop poor alignment? It can be caused by poor posture, e.g. slouching; prolonged periods of sitting; poor footwear, e.g. high heels; overuse (overused muscles become stronger and shorter and create a one-sided pull on a joint); weak core muscles; occupational activities; or injuries.

Physical damage is inevitable, but we can work to correct and diminish its negative effects. You might recognise this scenario: you were out for a run last week and towards the end, as your body grew fatigued, your posture deteriorated and, after you finished, you noticed a niggle in your knee/shin/foot/ankle. You gave yourself a rest day and tried a few easy miles the following day only to find the niggle was now a pain and you couldn't complete the three miles around the block you had planned. When this happens a visit to a physio is usually on the cards. Often this becomes multiple visits.

However, many form-related injuries can be avoided with your *IST Programme* and, if your budget allows, an additional regular treatment. For me that extra treatment is Amatsu, a Japanese-style therapy sometimes called Posture Correctional Therapy. Working gently with your muscles, tendons, fascia, ligaments and organs, the treatment helps to realign your key mechanical structures. In the build-up to a race, I aim to include one treatment monthly. If you're lucky enough to have someone offering this service within your community, I would recommend looking into it. Otherwise, many runners include regular massage in their programme.

Score yourself 4 points for completing your *IST Programme* or having a complementary treatment
Max: 4 points weekly

Mental Resilience

According to Chrissie Wellington, world triathlon champion and author of *A Life Without Limits*, pain is little more than a conversation between your body and your brain. Therefore, it is imperative to train your brain as well as your body.

Dr Olivia Hurley, sport psychologist and author of *Sport Cyberpsychology*, describes resilience as *the ability to persevere, to try to overcome setbacks*.

Mental strength develops when a person goes through trying times and comes out more resilient. Think of it as being like a muscle, something each of us can improve with training. This type of muscle allows athletes to last longer on days when they don't feel it. Mental strength is about awareness, resilience and determination.

Concentration is a skill. Concentration is never really lost, it is misplaced, allowed to wander or misdirected. Training your mind, as well as your body, to cope with fatigue, and learning to perceive it positively, may be just as important as how far and how fast you run in training. For me, a lot of this only came with experience. But psychological toughness and physical strength go hand in hand – the more you experience fatigue during your training, the more both your body and mind get used to dealing with it. There is a saying: *the more I sweat in training, the less I bleed in battle.*

In your day-to-day life you can train your mental resilience. Try doing things that make you uncomfortable like running in the rain, swimming regularly in the cold sea, switching to a cold shower each morning for a set time before stepping out. Do the hard things in your day first. Be accountable, deal with your problems, be positive and guard your thoughts.

To prepare yourself for the unexpected, vary your training times and choose sessions that throw you out of your rhythm. Make these as uncomfortable as you can, e.g. getting out of bed at 3 a.m. for a running session, or running on sore muscles the day after a long and gruelling run.

You need to know that when it comes to it you will overcome your thoughts of stopping when you fatigue. You need to know that when you feel more uncomfortable than you have ever felt, you will not stop. You need to know that stopping because of pain is not an option. Knowing you have that strength goes a long way to building confidence and mental toughness.

Some of the things I have learnt:

▶ The stronger the why, the more chance you will figure out the how. Mental toughness is all about diving into and surviving the how. It's a way we are seeking, not an excuse. To remind yourself of your why before every long run or every hill session can be a big motivator. It certainly works for me.

▶ To be an endurance runner you need to be brave and you can't be brave without being vulnerable. When you decide to take risks, you must be prepared to fail. These failures build you and remake you a stronger person. Failure is not a reason to list your shortcomings but a reason to celebrate your bravery.

► One big mistake I made was letting goals become expectations that weighed me down so much I almost suffocated. Goals can change. Attaching my self-worth to my goals was something that took me a few years to shake. My goals this year, or any other, do not determine who I am or my self-worth. I had to remove my ego from the mix.

Score yourself 1 point if you have a daily activity that pushes you out of your comfort zone, like a two-minute cold shower, or 5 points for a big event like getting out of bed in the middle of the night to run. Use your best judgement as to how much mental strength you are using.
Max: 7 points weekly

Visualisation

Athletes make use of numerous tactics adapted by sport psychologists to strengthen their resilience and mental skills. One is mental practice, the cognitive practice of a function in the absence of obvious bodily motion. When a runner practises the final mile of a race by thinking it through, or when a drummer practises a drum solo by visualising it, that is mental practice.

Visualisation gives athletes a sense of being successful and overcoming difficult parts of races before they actually go through them. It allows them to find solutions to in-race problems like the desire to slow down, walk, or stop, while also setting positive expectations and rehearsing a positive outcome.

Visualisation is concentrated dreaming. It's mind over matter. Think of what you are wearing in the race, the buzz of the people around you, the sound of the gun, your accelerated heart rate. If you're racing in your hometown or have previewed the course, use that to your advantage and make your visualisation as detailed as possible. By conjuring up these emotions, sights and sounds, you can prepare yourself to remain calm and collected and execute your race plan in a chaotic environment. The more specific you can be with the sights, sounds and emotions, the calmer and more confident you'll be on race day. It's been well documented that high confidence correlates to an increased level of performance. When it does happen, it will feel like you have done this before. Visualisation builds courage.

Discover what you long for and visualise it every chance you get. You may be amazed at how that personal focus will propel you in directions and at speeds you didn't think were possible for you. Visualisation can make things happen.

10 minutes of visualisation a day will increase your chances of success. You can practice when commuting, walking, running or lying on the kitchen floor. Visualisation is a habit you can develop that will impact nearly every aspect of your life. In the plan I suggest actively working on it twice a week.

'False hope syndrome' can lead to feelings of disappointment that follow chasing an unattainable goal. Overconfidence and an unrealistic degree of optimism can encourage people to waste time and effort on unfounded goals. Clearly someone who has poor eyesight may not make a great pilot or someone who is too light may not make a great sumo wrestler.

However, sometimes, the goals we set are not big enough, as we saw in the 1984 Olympic Games. Charlie Spedding was representing Great Britain in the marathon in the Los Angeles Olympics. Throughout his whole career, his dream had been to win an Olympic medal. He had been visualising it for years. He ran competitively from age 16 and made the Olympic team at age 32. The final stage of the marathon finished in the LA Memorial Coliseum stadium. Carlos Lopes from Portugal crossed the finish line for gold, setting a new Olympic record of 2:09:21, followed by Ireland's John Treacy who took silver in 2:09:56 and, two seconds later, Spedding whose time of 2:09:58 earned him the bronze. Spedding commented in his biography, *From Last to First: A Long-Distance Runner's Journey from Failure to Success*: *I just think it's interesting that I had a long-term goal, which for most of my career was ridiculously ambitious, but in the last few minutes it wasn't high enough.*

Score yourself 1 point for each active visualisation session you complete
Max: 2 points weekly

Self-talk

Self-talk is an incredibly powerful psychological skill that can be used to shape the internal, subconscious beliefs we hold about ourselves. It is also a cognitive tool used to influence our emotional state in order to improve our actions.

What we say, either in the privacy of our own minds or aloud to the world, has a direct impact on ourselves and our beliefs. I once heard that each and every cell in our body is perfectly and absolutely aware of our thoughts, feelings and beliefs, so we are reacting to our thoughts and beliefs on a cellular level. The opinions of others don't decide who we are; who we are is decided by what we tell ourselves.

When you are anxious, what you say to yourself tends to veer towards the sarcastic and hostile. Although understandable, this rarely improves a situation according to John Kremer and Aidan P. Moran, authors of *Pure Sport: Practical Sport Psychology*, published in 2008. When using self-talk, guidance and encouragement, in the sense of positive reinforcement, is a lot more effective than beating yourself up.

For the Tralee Marathon in 2014 I tried to change the way I thought and turn my regular negative narrative to positive talk. It was my fifth marathon, set in the south of Ireland in County Kerry. It was the first time I had used positive self-talk to help me achieve a goal. Mentally it was the hardest thing I had ever attempted.

In previous marathons I had fallen apart around the 20-mile mark, partly due to inadequate fitness and training, partly due to poor race-day nutrition and partly due to poor mental strength. Now, at mile 21, I felt totally spent. All my energy was gone and my knee started to pain me. *Oh God, here I go again,* I thought, *there's always the next time.*

But then I changed my self-talk. At that stage I hadn't learnt anything about what works and what doesn't but I was getting there. *Actually no, no way, not today,* I thought. *I will give this my everything and if I don't make it, I don't make it.* I switched my focus from the finish time to the next step. *If my knee snaps, it snaps,* I said to myself, *but I am going to find out if I have this inside me.* I started to quote a well-rehearsed, simple mantra: *I am strong, I am trained, I am ready for this.* I said it over and over and over, trying to block out all the negative thoughts. My speed picked up and within a few miles I was back on track. I had pain like I have never had physical pain but I was looking at it differently. Through my thoughts I managed to override it, to separate it from my focus, which was to keep my legs moving as fast as I could until I reached the finish line. I finished the marathon, within four hours, as if in someone else's body. It was an extraordinary feeling of mental strength.

Take note of what you are telling yourself when you are running. If you are filling your head with negative self-talk this will transfer to your performance. As your confidence drops, you will start to lose your technique and posture and become heavier on your feet. We need to be able to fill our heads with positive images and affirmations to keep us strong, tall, confident and relaxed when we need it most.

Be mindful of your words and realise that you can change your thoughts. A simple change from saying *I am...* to *You are...* adds to the power. *You are on top of this, you've got this* is stronger than *I'm on top of this, I've got this.* Our opinion of ourselves goes up and down with our mood, so telling yourself *I am strong* might be followed by a judgemental, *Yeah, right.* However, when we use third-person language like *You are strong* we get more benefit, in the same way we do when someone gives us a compliment. If you practice this regularly you will get better at it. To be aware of negative self-talk and to have the strength to eliminate it or put it aside could be invaluable during a 100-mile race.

World champion boxer Muhammad Ali was big into self-talk. There is a video clip on YouTube where Ali is training before the *Rumble in the Jungle*, the famous fight with George Foreman, and he talks himself through the upcoming fight: *Keep dancing, tire him out...*

I am a runner because I run. But just because I run doesn't mean endurance or mental toughness comes easily. I practice mental skills when training, which takes a little more than randomly tossing in a few positive words or a rehearsed mantra once my run hits a rough patch. Mentally tough athletes are positive thinkers and process-oriented. It took me a lot of reading and running to realise that the trick to finishing races in times that I was happy with was to focus on the process, not the time. The Düsseldorf Marathon in 2016 was part of my training for my first ultra. I wasn't worried or focused on the finish time too much, but I trained consistently and followed my training plan faithfully, and as a result I managed to run my fastest marathon.

Sport psychology techniques and exercises take practice and will only work on race day if you integrate them into your training. When you start driving a car for the first time you have to consciously think of everything. After a lot of practice and repetition you find you are able to reverse out of a driveway while chatting to your kids sitting in the back, all at the same time. The skill set required to drive has moved into your subconscious. When mental toughness becomes part of your subconscious you are on the right track.

When training for a race it helps me to regularly sit down and review my progress and realise that I am getting closer to the goal. I use a wall calendar and I write every run on it, including my weekly total. So at a glance I can see how many miles I have put in.

Use each long run as a chance for positive self-talk and build self-belief and confidence.

Score yourself 5 points for being mindful of your self-talk during your long run
Max: 5 points weekly

Hydration

Maintaining hydration as a runner is important for health and performance. Water regulates our body temperature, removes waste, helps bring energy to our cells and cushions our joints. Adequate hydration can improve recovery, minimise injury and cramping, and maximise performance.

After oxygen, water is a close second on the list of life essentials. We lose water through urinating and breathing and, of course, sweating. Dehydration causes your blood volume to drop, which lowers your body's ability to transfer heat and forces your heart to beat faster as your oxygen-carrying capacity drops, making it difficult for your body to meet aerobic demands. A dehydrated runner can experience lack of coordination, thirst, fatigue, dry mouth, cramps or spasms, headache and nausea.

The few days before a long run I make a conscious effort to hydrate. I have often been told that if you drink a lot before a run you can drink less during that run. That is not the case, not in my experience. What you should be doing is arriving hydrated to a run, then continuing to top up during it. Your body is an efficient machine. If you try to overfill it, it will get rid of the excess. Give it just what it needs and it'll work optimally.

Most runners know about sodium, but sweat also contains magnesium and potassium, which play a pivotal role in maintaining fluid balance and muscle function. A deficiency in either mineral can exacerbate the symptoms of dehydration and cause muscle cramps. To ensure you don't start a race deficient of magnesium, you should regularly eat leafy greens, almonds, pumpkin seeds, tofu, flaxseeds, broccoli and lentils. I also take a magnesium supplement each night before bed. For potassium, bananas, sweet potatoes, beets, tomatoes, oranges and pomegranate juice are good. For a long race like an ultra I take salt capsules or effervescent tablets with electrolytes – sodium, magnesium and potassium – to replace what's lost through sweat. Take note of the specific conditions of a given training or race day. Hot and humid conditions mean that replenishing your fluids and sodium levels is even more important.

The earliest signs of dehydration may be dark-coloured urine or a slight headache. As the condition worsens, you may feel extreme thirst, debilitating muscle cramps, fatigue and sometimes even a decrease in heart rate. It's necessary to recognise and listen to these signs because dehydration can do more than hurt your race performance – it can be life-threatening.

One way to determine your hydration status is to weigh yourself, without clothing, before and after a long run. If you've only lost 1 to 2% of your body weight, you're in a good place. If you've lost more than 2 or 3%

of your body weight, try drinking more during your long runs and drink water more regularly on the day before your run.

As with many of these areas of focus, practicing in training will pay off on race day. It wasn't until my fourth ultramarathon that I started using a hydration pack, sometimes called a water bladder backpack. Designed to carry your water, with a handy integrated drinking straw so you can drink while you run, they usually have a little extra space to carry some other essential race supplies and food. My early ultramarathons were all loop races so I was never too far from my support team; however, hydration packs were mandatory for the Belfast 2 Dublin event. Wearing one does mean that you may have a hot and sweaty back, but the benefit of being able to run without fear of dehydration far outweighs the downside.

Check out your race requirements early. See if there are any instructions on what you must carry at all times. If you are going to be self-sufficient for long sections of the race, invest in a hydration pack early in your training and wear it on all your long runs.

Hydration is a daily habit and some experts recommend eight glasses, or two litres, on a 'normal' day, increasing when you are in unusually hot or humid conditions or exercising. Set your daily target accordingly.

Score yourself 1 point for each day you reach your target water intake
Max: 7 points weekly

Discipline and Consistency

In the Oxford Dictionary, *discipline* is defined as the ability to control your behaviour or the way you live, work, etc., and *consistency* as the quality of always behaving in the same way or of having the same opinions, standards, etc.

Discipline and consistency are the two keys to health and fitness. You may achieve your goals without them, but when you're chasing something big, or life-changing, they are absolutely essential. They also go hand in hand. Without discipline, it's hard to be consistent in your actions. Without consistency, the mental practice of discipline will weaken over time. People who are disciplined do not skip runs because it's raining or slip back into eating an unhealthy diet because they are able to control their behaviour. They can live by the rules and goals they set for themselves. A disciplined runner follows the training plan, even if they are tired and sore and comfy in a nice warm bed. A disciplined healthy eater eats well at every meal even when it's easier not to. Discipline helps you make the right choice for your goals every day and keeps you consistent. Consistency beats natural ability. The best predictor of a runner's success is not usually talent, it's the volume of miles run. Knowing your *why* helps make these decisions less of a punishment and more of a joy.

It gets a lot easier to make the right food choices, whether it's adding vegetables to your meals or cooking in rather than ordering out, if you are consistent with it. Practicing positive self-talk and eliminating the voice of doubt in your head will help you be more disciplined. You can increase your discipline when you take full responsibility for yourself and refuse to accept excuses.

Most marathon runners have developed some level of discipline and consistency. Without either, they wouldn't have made it to where they are. The events for which I was most disciplined, the Düsseldorf and Vienna marathons and the Connemara 100, have been my most successful.

The most important thing which separates successful sports people from the rest of us is consistency in training: showing up and following a pre-decided plan no matter what the weather is like or how tired they feel. Through being consistent, you'll notice a huge improvement in your physical fitness. Because your body gets used to regular workouts, it conditions itself accordingly.

What we do day-to-day makes us who we are. What you practice consistently is what makes you yourself. A consistent running programme makes you a fitter, stronger person along with building your self-discipline and confidence. There is a tremendous sense of achievement when you pick a goal, choose a plan, develop the discipline and consistency to do it, and achieve it.

Score yourself 1 point for each day you achieve what you set out to do
Max: 7 points weekly

Laughter

When John Turner and Geoffrey Parsons added the lyrics *Smile, though your heart is aching* to the Charlie Chaplin music, I wonder if they knew how true those words are. We've all heard the phrase *laughter is the best medicine*, but when was the last time your doctor prescribed it? Well, I'm no doctor, but I am going to suggest you take a serious look at having a good laugh every day.

As children, we used to laugh dozens of times a day, but as we grow older we become more guarded and lose our knack of reacting spontaneously. We grow more serious, and laughter becomes more infrequent. By seeking out more opportunities for humour and laughter, we can add years to our lives. Laughter relaxes the whole body and can relieve physical tension and stress. It is known to decrease stress hormones and boost the immune system, increasing immune cells and infection-fighting antibodies, thus improving your resistance to disease. Laughter triggers the release of endorphins, the body's natural feel-good chemicals. Endorphins promote an overall sense of well-being and can even temporarily relieve pain.

I have several go-to YouTube clips that I watch when I feel like a laugh is needed. Rhod Gilbert, a Welsh comedian, has one on *lost luggage* that currently cracks me up, while the Irish comedian Tommy Tiernan usually manages to make me laugh regardless of my mood. When running, laughter is great for taking you out of yourself, often offering some much needed pain relief. At a lot of marathons and ultras you will see humorous signs being held up by supporters like, *For someone who runs all the time, you make it look like it's the first time you've ever tried*, and *If you've always wanted to try chafing, here's your chance*, and *Ultra-running: just like running, but slower, longer and more sad and lonely*. The best are the ones that catch you off guard, and even take a minute to get. It can have you chuckling for miles.

Humour can be improved and even learned. You can start by spending time with the right people and by not taking yourself so seriously. If you make a decision to bring more humour into your day, you can't go far wrong.

Score yourself 1 point for days when you remember having a good old laugh
Max: 7 points weekly

Number 21[2]: Know Your *Why*

My first book, *The Plant-Based Runner*, tells my story of how I went from struggling to run three miles around the block to completing the Belfast 2 Dublin 107-mile race. In the opening pages I included 35 reasons why someone should read the book, including:

- ▶ You want to love yourself
- ▶ You are angry at the cards you have been dealt
- ▶ You are ready to take responsibility
- ▶ You want to be a skinny bitch

It was a light-hearted list, and I had a little fun writing it, but the reason I included it was serious. Knowing your *why*, whether you're giving up smoking, training for your first 5km park run or planning your first ultra, is the secret sauce. Having a clear and compelling personal reason to undertake this challenge is the final piece of the puzzle.

What you're committing to here is an 8-month training plan. That's two-thirds of the year ahead. 24 weekends when your long runs will take precedence over a late night out with friends. All those days when watching the latest episode of your favourite show will take second place behind putting on your running shoes and clocking up some more miles. Countless times when you'll wonder if your *why* is really worth it.

So stop here, take a moment, and write it down. Dog-ear the corner and come back to this page as often as you need to. What you write next will see you through around 1,000 miles of training.

Why....

---

2   It isn't one of the 20 focus areas because it's not something you can actively do each week, but without it, you're unlikely to succeed.

Putting It All Together

It's easy to read the 20 sections above and think, *Sleep, yeah, I already have a good routine around that, hydration, yep, no bother, eight glasses a day*, and so forth, but what does it look like when you put it all together? Only you can decide.

I think of the 20 areas in smaller groups of similar activities. The first group are all the running and movement activities: stretching, recovery run, hill/fartlek, regular runs, long run, alternative exercise and the *IST Programme*.

Start by planning your five runs for the week based on your own schedule. Add in your cross-training activity on one of the days you're not running, between your recovery run and hill/fartlek day. In terms of activities, you're also going to want to add in your *IST* circuits once a week and stretching at least twice a week. If you look at the example of the completed *Peak Performance Chart* (Section Two, weeks 9-32); you'll see that with five runs a week and one day with cross-training, there is only one true rest day. Keep that day totally free of activities and your second rest day will have low activity as it falls on your recovery run day.

You may already be doing a lot of what's in the rest of the plan. If you're someone like me, all the food sections (planning, shopping, preparation, eating and hydration) will already be in your weekly routine, but focusing on them will give you the opportunity to improve them. In particular, figuring out what prepares you for, fuels you through and helps you recover after your long runs will be invaluable.

When it comes to the mental aspects of the training plan, I group visualisation and self-talk together as activities that I will actively focus on when I'm out and running so they don't have to take up additional time in the day. While mental resilience may be something I habit-stack by tagging a two-minute blast of cold water onto the end of my daily shower.

You will have to set aside some time for the education element. This might be my favourite of all the 20 activities as I get a real buzz from learning how other people approach ultra-running or reading up on performance optimisation through nutrition.

If you're looking for more ways to group a few activities together, make reading part of your bedtime routine and that's education and sleep sorted.

Once all that's done, you're left with laughter and discipline and consistency to look at. If you're doing everything you set out to do, discipline and consistency look after themselves and if you live in a house like mine, you're going to have a good laugh every day (even if that usually means laughing at myself). If laughter doesn't come so easily, check in with yourself as part of your bedtime routine and if you can't remember whether you laughed or not, take a minute and find something funny like the YouTube clip of comedian Kevin Bridges on the TV show *Would I Lie to You?* when he accidentally bought a horse.

So that's it. Think of it as your own accountability partner. If you can take responsibility for each small, daily action, very soon you will have a week of accomplishments under your belt. In eight months' time, as you stand on the start line of your ultra, remember where you started, how far you've come, and that the work you've put in has prepared you for success.

Training Plans for Your First 100-Mile Race

Each weekly review of your training plan should ratify that you are heading in the right direction. There may be setbacks along the way, there usually are, but with regular analysis of your progress you can adapt the plan and approach race day confident in the belief that you can achieve that goal. I have discovered that this sense of belief in your training plan is the cornerstone for keeping positive during the long lead up to an event.

Control what you can control but accept that there are certain things that you cannot take responsibility for. Being nervous and anxious uses up valuable energy. It's natural to feel nervous on the days leading up to the race or the morning of the event, but if you're getting the jitters every time you think of the race during the months of training, you'll exhaust yourself. Trust in your training, work on developing your belief and confidence, and encourage your positive mindset by focusing on what is in your control.

The training programme is when it gets exciting. It's the tofu in the sandwich. There are two training plans included for your first 100-miler: the

Minimum Training Plan and the *Advanced Training Plan*. Both will get you through your first 100-mile race; which you choose should be determined by your starting baseline. I used the *Minimum Training Plan* for my first successful 100-miler.

This is the time to try out everything. And I mean everything.

First off is your shoes. Make sure your feet and legs feel good after your long runs. If not, try changing your shoes. My choice of running shoes for long runs are the Bondi range from Hoka One One. They are well padded and offer great protection for anyone training for an ultra, especially when you are in your fifties and want to give your body every protection that you can. I wear 1000-Mile socks that I know always feel good and don't make me blister. One time before a race I was buying socks and the shop had sold out of 1000-Mile socks. The owner suggested another pair and, because I trusted him, I bought them and I wore them and I blistered. I'm sure they were great socks for him but they were a disaster for me.

Three years ago I ran the Armagh Marathon in Northern Ireland wearing a running shirt that I had never worn before. All was fine until there was some heavy rain. I put on a rain jacket for the last few miles and in the finish photos my yellow jacket has two red spots where my nipples were and two red blood lines down to my waist. The running shirt got wet and heavy and started to rub off my nipples. By the time I crossed the line the blood had come through my shirt and jacket. Every shower hurt for a week. I always use a roll-on protective gel or Vaseline on my nipples but this shirt rubbed it off. Check out everything personally. No-one will be running your races for you.

Runners should not increase their mileage more than 10% week to week. In other words, if you ran 30 miles one week, increase it to 33 miles the following week but no more. A methodical and slow progression of mileage helps to ward off injuries and improve performance.

This book is all about recognising the components of a successful ultra-marathon plan and implementing them. Learning the factors for success is one thing, but we also need to know how to address them in training. Each plan needs to have sustainable mileage with down weeks for rest and recovery. You need to be consistent.

Too often, runners select a plan that they would *like* to be able to stick to. The wiser move is to select a plan that you *will* be able to stick to and allow for some flexibility. It is a guideline; stick to it as best you can. Some days you will have to be flexible and switch things around. Nothing is perfect – go with it. Remember, life continues outside your plan. For me, it's important to have balance between family life, work and running. If my love life isn't working, it won't take long before the rest caves in.

The long runs are there to fatigue the leg muscles and build leg durability. They help you to learn to burn more fat and spare your limited carbohydrate stores. The long runs give you the essential time to practice fuelling and they expose your body and brain to suffering and pain. Dropping the mileage every fourth week is a common way to reduce injuries.

Back-to-back long runs are long runs that you run on consecutive days. They are a great alternative to running distances in one day that will take too long to recover from. These back-to-back long runs help develop strong legs and a strong mind – both key to a successful ultramarathon. At first these can be rough, but with consistency your body and mind will adapt.

Before you start either of these training plans you should be at marathon fitness. That is, you should have run several marathons and be currently fit enough to comfortably run 12 miles. The *Minimum Training Plan* is mainly under 55 miles per week; the more advanced plan, under 70 miles. You will know yourself which is right for you. Work, family and other life commitments will determine how much time you have each week to get out and run the miles. Both plans include five runs each week.

In both plans, from week five you will start to include hill runs on your Wednesday run and alternate with fartlek runs from then until week 21. Weeks shaded grey represent reduced mileage weeks which will help reduce the chance of injury and exhaustion. As with all training plans, adjust the days you run to suit your own schedule but try to keep the sequence of run days and rest days.

All figures are in miles. If, however, you are used to training in kilometres, I have included these charts converted to kilometres in the appendix.

Minimum Training Plan (miles)

Week	Mon	Tue	Wed*	Thu	Fri	Sat	Sun	Total	*Wed
1	3 + stretch	Cross-train	5	6	Rest	12	5	31	
2	3 + stretch	Cross-train	5	6	Rest	14	5	33	
3	3 + stretch	Cross-train	5	6	Rest	16	5	35	
4	3 + stretch	Cross-train	3	5	Rest	14	5	30	
5	3 + stretch	Cross-train	5	7	Rest	16	7	38	Hills
6	3 + stretch	Cross-train	5	7	Rest	18	7	40	Fartlek
7	3 + stretch	Cross-train	5	7	Rest	18	10	43	Hills
8	3 + stretch	Cross-train	5	6	Rest	14	7	35	Fartlek
9	3 + stretch	Cross-train	5	7	Rest	21	5	41	Hills
10	3 + stretch	Cross-train	5	7	Rest	14	12	41	Fartlek
11	3 + stretch	Cross-train	5	7	Rest	24	6	45	Hills
12	3 + stretch	Cross-train	5	6	Rest	18	5	37	Fartlek
13	3 + stretch	Cross-train	5	7	Rest	20	10	45	Hills
14	3 + stretch	Cross-train	5	3	Rest	27	Rest	38	Fartlek
15	3 + stretch	Cross-train	4	7	Rest	14	10	38	Hills
16	3 + stretch	Cross-train	5	7	Rest	25	10	50	Fartlek
17	3 + stretch	Cross-train	5	7	Rest	27	12	54	Hills
18	3 + stretch	Cross-train	5	7	Rest	14	10	39	Fartlek
19	3 + stretch	Cross-train	Rest	3	Rest	50	Rest	56	
20	3 + stretch	Cross-train	5	6	Rest	14	5	33	Hills
21	3 + stretch	Cross-train	Rest	7	Rest	24	14	48	
22	3 + stretch	Cross-train	7	5	Rest	18	Rest	33	
23	3 + stretch	Cross-train	Rest	7	Rest	10	5	25	
24	3 + stretch	Cross-train	4	Rest	2	100	-	109	

Advanced Training Plan (miles)

Week	Mon	Tue	Wed*	Thu	Fri	Sat	Sun	Total	*Wed
1	5 + stretch	Cross-train	6	7	Rest	12	5	35	
2	5 + stretch	Cross-train	6	7	Rest	14	6	38	
3	5 + stretch	Cross-train	6	8	Rest	16	6	41	
4	5 + stretch	Cross-train	5	7	Rest	14	5	36	
5	5 + stretch	Cross-train	6	8	Rest	18	8	45	Hills
6	5 + stretch	Cross-train	6	8	Rest	18	12	49	Fartlek
7	5 + stretch	Cross-train	8	6	Rest	20	10	49	Hills
8	5 + stretch	Cross-train	5	7	Rest	14	6	37	Fartlek
9	5 + stretch	Cross-train	6	8	Rest	20	12	51	Hills
10	5 + stretch	Cross-train	6	10	Rest	16	14	51	Fartlek
11	5 + stretch	Cross-train	6	8	Rest	24	12	55	Hills
12	5 + stretch	Cross-train	6	8	Rest	16	10	45	Fartlek
13	5 + stretch	Cross-train	6	10	Rest	18	14	53	Hills
14	5 + stretch	Cross-train	6	4	Rest	31	Rest	46	Fartlek
15	5 + stretch	Cross-train	6	10	Rest	16	10	47	Hills
16	5 + stretch	Cross-train	6	10	Rest	25	15	61	Fartlek
17	5 + stretch	Cross-train	6	10	Rest	25	18	64	Hills
18	5 + stretch	Cross-train	6	12	Rest	16	10	49	Fartlek
19	5 + stretch	Cross-train	6	4	Rest	50	Rest	65	Hills
20	5 + stretch	Cross-train	6	10	Rest	30	20	71	Fartlek
21	5 + stretch	Cross-train	6	8	Rest	30	20	69	Hills
22	5 + stretch	Cross-train	6	10	Rest	15	15	51	
23	5 + stretch	Cross-train	6	8	Rest	10	5	34	
24	5 + stretch	Cross-train	4	Rest	2	100	-	111	

The View from the Crew Car

asked Fiona to write a small piece about what happens during an ultra from the perspective of the crew. I was thinking 300 to 500 words. She came back with something a little longer, just over 10,000 words. I gave her the look, over the top of my glasses, and her reply was, *It's a big job*, which it is.

The following captures it perfectly and gives you an insight into 28 hours on the road. If you are thinking of crewing for a friend it would be a good idea to read this. Similarly, if you are thinking of asking someone to crew for you, this will help you understand just what you are asking.

Connemara 100, Ireland, 8–9 August 2020

As I drove out of the mechanic's yard, tears streamed down my face. All of the anxiety and feelings of failure over the past seven hours had to come out if I was going to be able to support Jonathan in what would be the more difficult hours that lay ahead.

We both ran our first marathon together in Rome in 2010. My running experience after that was sporadic and inconsistent – I ran a half-marathon in Vienna in 2017, while Jonathan ran the full, and we both ran the Moscow Marathon later that year. One might think I only lace up my trainers with the promise of foreign shores and exciting travels. One wouldn't be wrong. Meanwhile, Jonathan had continued to run and race regularly in the years between. He had run 15 marathons and five ultramarathons. Connemara was to be his sixth.

Waking up in Clifden that morning I had been very clear on what my role was that day. We had prepared for this. In fact we had prepared for this race more than any race before. Jonathan's preparation had begun the moment he first read about this race. These challenges plant themselves in his subconscious and germinate there. By the time the leaves break through to be seen, the roots are already established. Other races that came between then and now were all part of the preparation. Miles of training, often early on Saturday and Sunday mornings, leaving me to roll over in bed and sleep late, were the norm. My preparation began in the final days and weeks leading up to the journey to Connemara in the west of Ireland. I knew the drill.

Because this was taking place in August 2020, when strict COVID-19 restrictions were in place in Ireland, the pre-race meetings took place on Zoom. Jonathan and I had visited the area earlier in the year to familiarise ourselves with the route. It was just before Ireland went into our first lockdown after the arrival of COVID-19 on the island.

During one of the Zoom calls Ray O'Connor, the race organiser, suggested that having your partner as your crew might not be the wisest move. He pointed out that your partner might not be the best person to encourage you to keep going when they can see the pain you're going through. I've always been very comfortable in the job. I'm not a sadist and I understand how it could be too much for others. Watching the one you love put themselves through such extreme misery and suffering is difficult to witness. But knowing the overwhelming sense of achievement it gives Jonathan makes me want to ensure that I do what I can to support him during those tortuous hours of the race. The rest is up to him. Jonathan makes sacrifices every day for his family. Being there for him in his hour[3] of need seems the least I can do.

Up until this race, I had taken on the sole responsibility of crewing Jonathan's races. That's not to say that I was always on my own; I regularly had great company on marathon day. I remember wonderful days in Düsseldorf finding spots to stop for coffee with Jonathan's big sister, Grace. We whiled away the hours chatting and walking as we tracked Jonathan around the course. Düsseldorf is a great course for supporters. My stepson Jem has kept me company in many races. He is the best companion and

---

3   If you choose to crew for someone you love, be prepared to be there for them for more than an 'hour' of need. Jonathan has participated in races that have taken 32 hours to complete.

encourages all runners in a race. We have been together during 100-mile races and marathons. During the Cork marathon the heavy winds and rain made for a miserable event, for the crew anyway. Yet we managed to laugh our way through it.

But this race was different. The Connemara 100-mile event is run on main roads that span an area of 192 square miles (498 square kilometres), and although Connemara is blessed with a tranquil and unspoiled landscape, there are stretches of road that carry a lot of fast east-west traffic and solitary runners would be at risk. It was a race requirement for each runner to have a car driving behind them, for the entire race, for protection. Clearly, as participants had up to 30 hours to complete the race, the demands were too much for one person; a second driver was needed. We had managed to secure two others, Emma and Alan.

Once the crew were on board, we set up a Zoom call to talk them through what they could expect. The race was to start at 6 a.m. on Saturday morning. We decided that I would do the first shift and Emma would take over at the 20-mile mark, sometime after 10 a.m. From there, we split the race into 10-mile segments alternating between drivers. Alan would join us at mile 50 on Saturday afternoon and was happy to take on the bulk of the night hours when I knew I would be flagging. Emma planned to join Jonathan en route and run some of the miles with him. Pacers are a huge help for runners. They distract from the pain and it was something Jonathan had never had the luxury of before. Knowing that Emma would be running some of the miles with him was a huge psychological boost.

We packed up our car on the Friday morning. The support vehicle had to have everything on board to sustain the runner. Connemara is so remote, there wouldn't be many opportunities to buy things along the way. We knew from previous races that a fresh hot coffee or a bag of chips (fries) in the dark of night could change everything for Jonathan. Because so much of what a runner goes through in an ultramarathon is mental, the lift that comes with an unexpected treat is immense and shouldn't be underestimated. Connemara wouldn't offer those possibilities.

Ultramarathons require an enormous amount of planning and preparation. A runner's appetite has a tendency to come and go throughout the race so we knew we needed a wide variety of food to alternately whet and satisfy it. If you're planning on serving any of it hot (like coffee or soup), then you're going to need a saucepan and camp stove too.

I'm sure there are places in the world where you know what sort of weather you'll encounter in a race, but those places are not in Ireland. As a result, you need clothes for every eventuality and plenty of them. Jonathan had been blister-free for most of his running career, but that had all changed in the Belfast 2 Dublin race. We were well prepared with a first aid kit that would deal with everything from blisters and muscle ache to stomach upset and sunburn. Finally, you need to remember all the little things that are easily forgotten in the rush to get on the road, items such as toilet rolls, phone chargers, head torches, spare batteries, salt tablets and don't forget the kitchen sink.

Here's a full list of what we packed:

KITCHEN:
- ▶ portable camping stove and gas
- ▶ saucepan
- ▶ chopping board
- ▶ mugs, knives, forks and spoons (including a sharp knife)
- ▶ bowls, plates
- ▶ stick blender (we were going to make soup when we arrived at our accommodation on Friday night)
- ▶ coffee press
- ▶ dishcloth and tea towels
- ▶ dish soap

MISCELLANEOUS:
- ▶ magnetic car beacon (amber flashing light – a race requirement)
- ▶ flask (for soup and/or coffee)
- ▶ cooler box and ice packs (as the food would be in the car for up to 30 hours we needed to ensure it stayed fresh)

- 35-litre jerry can (Jonathan would need approximately 600ml water per hour for up to 30 hours which is 18 litres. I would need water for myself too.)
- solar shower (This was one of our new purchases. At Jonathan's previous ultra, he had gained a huge lift as morning dawned and he had porridge, brushed his teeth and had a full change of clothes. We figured that adding a shower to the mix would be pure bliss.)
- foldable camp chair
- washbag

FIRST AID:

- sun cream
- hydration tablets/salts
- anti-chafe stick
- first aid kit
- painkillers
- baby wipes
- toilet roll
- digestive enzymes
- blister treatment pack

ELECTRONIC/OTHER:

- chargers – phone, headphones, watch
- head torches
- batteries
- running sunglasses
- other glasses (reading, driving)
- arm-band phone holder

CLOTHES:

- 4 x raincoats/light running jackets
- 4 x pairs of runners
- 5 x pairs of socks

- 14 x short-sleeve or vest running shirts
- 4 x long-sleeve running shirts
- 4 x pairs of running shorts
- 3 x Under Armour cold weather compression tops (for night-time)
- gloves
- warm hat
- sun hat
- snood
- extra laces
- compression stockings (for the day after the race)

FOOD:

- potatoes (to be cooked the night before the race)
- soup ingredients (sweet potato and coconut, recipe later in the book)
- salted crisps
- dolmades (stuffed vine/grape leaves. Although we usually buy these fresh from our local farmer's market, we found the canned ones easier to transport. We brought 12 cans, about 120 dolmades.)
- peanut butter (on apple slices or crackers with a sprinkle of salt is a tasty snack)
- apples
- melon
- bananas
- vegan sausages (during Jonathan's months of training, he found sausage sandwiches quite easy to eat and digest)
- gluten-free bread
- coconut oil
- vegan mayonnaise
- coffee
- rice milk
- gluten-free brown pasta and vegan pesto (for a simple Friday night dinner)

▶ Sunwarrior protein and shake ingredients (recovery protein drink recipe later in book)

SUPPORT CREW ITEMS:

▶ duvet and pillow (to cosy up in the car for a snooze)

▶ camera

▶ laptop

▶ book

That Friday, the sun was beating down and the temperature was 19°C. As we neared Clifden we turned off the main road to follow the route the final miles the race would take along the coast into the town. Based on our calculations, Jonathan would be on this section of the route between the hours of 1 a.m. and 7 a.m. on Sunday morning. I figured that he would be better prepared knowing what to expect. The road undulated for miles without many flat stretches. And each time the road rose ahead, the mood in the car went downhill. By the time we reached our destination Jonathan was miserable. He started to question his preparedness for the challenge that lay ahead. We had booked a two-bed apartment for ourselves and Emma and it had a kitchen which we needed for making soup and other food for race day. We checked in and unloaded the car.

Clifden is located on the west coast of Ireland and is a popular tourist destination and base for exploring the area. The town itself is compact and all the main pubs, shops and restaurants are located around the town square – well, triangle really. That Friday evening, the sun was shining and the tables outside the pubs and restaurants were busy with people enjoying a rare warm Irish summer evening. Due to the strict COVID-19 restrictions, seating indoors and outdoors was limited but we managed to get two seats up at the bar in a place that had a good selection of vegan and gluten-free food. As we were finishing dinner Emma rang to say she had arrived and was going to the apartment.

Jonathan took the car and drove to the local petrol station to fill it up. The last thing I needed was to run out of petrol on a deserted stretch of road in the middle of the race. I sat with Emma talking about her drive and the unusual weather. The forecast for the weekend was hot and it was expected to hit 24°C. Jonathan and I still had a bit of organising to do so we headed to the kitchen to make soup, sandwiches and boil potatoes. We had brought a 35-litre jerry can that had to be filled with drinking water, and I needed Jonathan to carry it back down the narrow stairs to the car as I wouldn't be able to manage it on my own. Jonathan laid out the running gear he would be starting in and attached his race number to the leg of his shorts with his bib magnets.

Prep complete, we headed to bed and hoped for a good night's sleep. I've read that the sleep you get the night before a race doesn't impact on performance, but there's nothing worse than lying awake for hours on end waiting for sleep, or morning, to come. Thankfully sleep came and we were woken by the alarm at 5.10 a.m. Jonathan showered and dressed while I made porridge. Knowing that we had a long day and night ahead of us, Emma wisely had stayed in bed. I knew that I would have a little time after the race started before I needed to get on the road. The race organisers ask you to wait until the runners are a few miles down the road so that there isn't a lot of congestion at the start. My plan was to meet Jonathan at mile five, about 55 minutes after the start.

The start line was just a few hundred metres from our apartment door so we strolled up at about 5.50 a.m. The Connemara 100 starts with an extended lap of the town, approximately one mile, before passing back across the start line and then heading north. A small crowd of supporters cheered the runners as they took off for their lap around the town. I waited until all the runners had completed their first mile and strolled back to the apartment, excited about what the next 30 hours would bring.

Anyone who knows me knows that I overestimate what I can complete in a given amount of time, or maybe I underestimate how long something will take me. Either way I am usually rushing to get everything done. I had a quick shower, packed up our overnight clothes and wash bag, and took the first of a number of trips up and down the stairs with all the weekend's food and paraphernalia. By the time the last of the bags were in the car I was feeling the pressure. It was already after 6.40 a.m. and Jonathan was expecting to see me in 15 minutes at mile five. I knew that it could be slow progress to find him along the course route as the roads in this part of Ireland are single lane and twist and turn to hug the coastline and mountains. As each runner would have their own crew car, it would take time to get past the runners that were behind Jonathan at this stage.

I hopped into the car and turned the key. Nothing. Not a sputter. Not a peep. Silence. I took the key out of the ignition, put it back in and tried again. *Is this how I usually start the car?* I wondered. I tried again. The car was silent but my blood was pounding in my ears. I felt sick. This was not in the plan. My mind started to race. *What would Jonathan do at mile five if I wasn't there?* I knew he wouldn't stop running, but would it distract him? He needed all his mental capacity to complete this race. It was already warm and Jonathan had left without any water. My first instinct was to call the race organisers. See if anyone was on the course that could get some water to him. An hour into the race he wouldn't be in any difficulty, but who knew how long it would be before I caught up with him. If he ran into difficulty at this early stage, his whole race could be in jeopardy. I wasn't ready to be responsible for that. There had been months of training to prepare himself for this race. Years, in fact. There are particular traits that you want in a support crew member. In that moment I felt like I was exhibiting none of them.

Thankfully, I wasn't alone. Emma was upstairs and I needed her. Jonathan and I have known Emma for almost 10 years. I like to think that I'm a good organiser and am suited to this type of task, but I'm not a patch on Emma. Emma is operations director with one of Ireland's leading hospitality companies. I knew Emma could solve this problem in her sleep. Just to be sure, though, I decided to wake her. She appeared at her bedroom door in her pyjamas.

Emma, my car won't start. I have jump leads in my car. Can we see if a jump-start will get it going?

Sure, give me five minutes.

Okay. I'll need to empty the boot to get to the jump leads. Come down when you're ready.

I went back to the car to undo all the packing I had finished just minutes before. I later found out that Emma's instinct in that moment was to think of what our options were. Worst-case scenario, she figured, we would put all the gear in her car and crew him together. With that in mind she made herself an espresso. Emma travels with her own espresso machine. Having lived in Italy for a few years in her twenties, coffee is an integral part of her morning routine. She got dressed and joined me on the road in front of the apartment.

Emma pulled the nose of her car up to mine but when she raised her car bonnet I was faced with an unfamiliar engine. I've always had old cars and am comfortable using jump leads but where was her battery? As we both took out our mobile phones to google her car and 'battery location' a bright yellow Mini Cooper came down the street towards us. The woman driving stopped, got out of the car and asked if she could help.

My car won't start and I'm usually good at jumping the battery, but I can't see her battery, I said desperately.

No problem, the woman said. *I build car engines in my spare time. Let me pull my car in, I'll jump it from my battery.*

Within two minutes my car was running. I knew what I had to do, rev the car a bit to get a little charge and then not switch it off until it had been running for a while or it would need another jump-start.

Thank you so much. I can't believe you came along when you did. Where do you work? I asked my guardian angel.

In the Alcock & Brown Hotel, she replied.

I made a mental note to send her a thank you card when this was all over. I said goodbye to Emma and headed off in pursuit of Jonathan.

The Connemara 100-mile race course is spectacular. I tried to take in the views as I wound my way along the first few miles. By the time I met the runner taking up the rear of the race it was long past 7 a.m. Jonathan would be at about mile eight by the time I reached him. I passed crew cars and runners, remembering to smile, wave and give a beep of encouragement to each as I went by.

Finally, I saw Jonathan's distinctive gait on the road ahead. For the first time since 6 a.m. I relaxed a little. My job this weekend was to be there for him. I had decided not to let him know that there had been any trouble. I caught up with him and gave a little beep to let him know I was behind him. We spotted the entrance to a house up ahead that would give me enough space to pull in off the road. He leaned in through the passenger window with a big smile on his face. But he only had to take one look at me to know something was wrong. My plan to keep the car issues to myself went out the window.

What's up? he said, knowingly.

The car battery was flat this morning. I had to get a jump-start. What do you fancy? Water? Something to eat? I replied, trying to change the subject.

Yes. Water and some vine leaves.

Jonathan went to the back of the car and opened the boot of the SUV.

Who drank all the water? he asked from behind me.

What? I asked, startled, thinking he was pulling my leg.

I turned off the car engine and joined him at the back of the car. The 35-litre jerry can was empty down to the level of the tap. When I put it back in the car I must have nudged the tap out of alignment. As I drove the miles from Clifden, the water had been pouring out the tap into the boot of the car.

Seriously? I asked the heavens.

I opened a can of vine leaves for Jonathan to eat and I prepared a small bottle of water with a hydration tablet in it. Jonathan could carry that and sip it over the next few miles. The carpet in the boot of the car was saturated. The boot of our car has a well where you can keep a spare wheel. Right now there was enough water to support a small village sloshing around in there. I estimated we were left with about eight litres. If I contacted Emma she could pick up water in Clifden before she left. I hopped back in the driver's seat and turned the key. It never dawned on me that I hadn't driven for long enough to charge the battery. It was dead again.

Can't a woman catch a break? I thought to myself.

Another crew car had pulled in behind us to support their runner, so I approached the driver and asked for help jump-starting the car again. Jonathan was ready to get going so I told him to head on and I would catch up with him shortly.

John, as I later found out he was called, pulled the front of his car up to mine. He managed to block the traffic in both directions, such was his angle. My car started. I would not be turning it off again. I thanked John and he passed the leads in the window to me. Hopefully I wouldn't be needing them again. I looked out my rearview mirror ready to drive and noticed Jonathan had left the back door open. I sat there, foot on the accelerator, revving the engine. I was stuck. There was no chance I was going to leave the car idling while I got out to close it. I could see a couple of runners coming up the road towards me. Running an ultra takes everything you've got. The smallest thing can throw you off course. Even though it would only take a moment, I felt that my role was to support the runners, not the other way round. Even now, as I write this, months later, I am still embarrassed at the next thing I did.

Can you help, please? I hollered out the window, *my car battery is dead and I'm afraid to take my foot off the accelerator to close the back door.*

The runners kindly obliged (like they had nothing better to be doing on mile eight of a 100-mile race).

I took a deep breath and headed on my way. I called Emma to update her on the water situation. Okay, one problem solved, now to think about the car. My car insurance included roadside assistance so I figured it was worth putting in a call. They could meet me on the route once Emma had taken over at mile 20. Maybe they could replace the battery. I rang the emergency number. It turns out roadside assistance like to know your location when you call. They are not big fans of moving targets. I asked how long it would take for assistance to arrive. He told me they could have someone with me at about 10.15 a.m.. I looked at the map. I knew there was a petrol station near mile 23 on the course. I gave that as my location as I knew I could be there to meet them. Okay, second problem solved. I crossed my fingers and hoped that would be the last of the problems for the weekend. I had caught up with Jonathan again.

You might have wondered what it's like to drive behind a runner for a 100-mile race. Slow, is the answer. On the advice of Ray, the race organiser, we had practiced once before on a 10-mile stretch. I couldn't get over how different it felt to 'normal' driving. I don't know how many races are run this way, but if you ever find yourself in one, I'd recommend a practice run. Not only do you, as the driver, need to slow down and give the runner enough room on the road that you're not clipping their heels, but you also need to stay close enough that another car can't get between you and the runner. The most terrifying moments for me were those when a car came screeching around the corner behind me, only to be met by me, almost at a standstill, holding up the road. I now knew why the Connemara 100 insisted on having a driver behind each runner for the entire race. Rural Irish roads barely have enough space for two cars, let alone two cars and a runner.

As this was Jonathan's sixth ultramarathon, we had a lot of data to plot his expected pace throughout the race. The first 50 miles would take 12 hours give-or-take. The second 50 miles would take 15 or 16 hours. So, at mile 15, we were going around four miles an hour. The route rolled along through the hilly landscape. I was terrified that the car would cut out crawling up the hills at such a slow speed behind Jonathan. It wailed as I revved the accelerator, overcompensating for the fear in the pit of my stomach.

But the miles passed and Jonathan was looking good. The sun beat down and I was glad that he had made a last-minute purchase in our local running shop, Runzone, to pick up a light sun cap. It was going to be a scorcher. It wasn't 10 a.m. yet and the temperature was touching 20°C. The road levelled out and a beautiful view across a lake opened up in front of us. I heard a 'beep-beep' from a car behind and glanced in my rearview mirror. Never before (or since) have I been happier to see someone. It was Emma. Early. The apprehension started to disappear. We drove along in convoy until we reached the 20-mile mark and another planned stop for Jonathan.

Emma had brought coffee, and plenty of water.

It's grand, Fiona, she said in her usual, calm way.

I relaxed and told her my plan about the roadside assistance. We decided to pack enough supplies in her car to see Jonathan through to 30 miles or more. Plenty of food, a couple of changes of clothes, sun lotion, first aid supplies, hydration tablets, wet wipes, a towel and toilet roll were transferred to her back seat. Jonathan munched on some more dolmades, changed his T-shirt, reapplied sun cream to the back of his neck and headed off on mile 21, one fifth of the race already complete. I got back into my car, happy to be handing over the reins to Emma for a while. I beeped Jonathan as I passed and headed the three short miles to the meeting point with the roadside assistance crew.

I pulled into the petrol station just a few hundred metres off the course route. There was a little shop in the station which made it a popular spot for support cars and crew to grab petrol with a side of ice cream. As I sat there looking intently up and down the road for something that resembled a tow truck or mechanic's van, I noticed a runner with a bib number.

You've missed the turn, I called out to him.

Although the route was run exclusively on roads, it was unmarked and you could easily miss a turn if you weren't paying attention. Thankfully, he was only 300 metres off track and I was glad that I had spotted him when I did and sent him back in the right direction. Fortunes were looking up.

The minutes ticked by and I called the roadside assistance number again.

They're on their way, was the suitably vague information they were willing to share.

It was then I noticed what had been staring me in the face the entire time I had been sitting in the forecourt. Straight across the road was the Kylemore Service Station. I turned off my engine and walked over to the mechanic who was just inside the garage door.

Do you see the Honda CR-V across the road? I asked, not for a minute thinking he was blind.

Yes, he said.

I don't suppose you have a battery for one? I said hopefully.

Afraid not, he said. *They have an unusual size battery.*

Of course they do, I thought.

Mortimers might, though, he said in a way that made me feel like I should know what or who Mortimers were. He must have realised I wasn't familiar with the battery wonderland he was describing by the blank look on my face. *Mortimers,* he repeated. *They're just five minutes up the road. I'd say they can sort you out.*

He gave me their number and I held my breath as I dialled. A friendly voice answered. I explained what I was looking for and told him the make and model of my car.

Yes, no problem, we have that in stock, he said, not knowing that he had just made my day.

Great, I chirped. *I'll be there in five.*

I was so relieved. I thanked the mechanic, headed back across to the car and hopped in, hopeful that the rest of the weekend would look a whole lot better in a few minutes' time. I turned the key.

Oh, come on!

I took another walk back across to the helpful mechanic.

Any chance you can give me a jump? I asked sheepishly.

No problem, I'll be across in a minute.

I sat back in the car and called to cancel the roadside assistance.

On the road again, after my third jump, I hoped my self-diagnosis was correct and a new battery was going to fix the problem. I would know soon enough. I pulled into the yard of Mortimers Garage and was met by a father and son team who looked over the sorry state of my battery. One test and the wry smile said it all. The battery was banjaxed and needed replacement. They'd have me back on the road in a jiffy. I asked if they had a bathroom I could use. You have to be comfortable with holding it or being at one with nature on an ultramarathon race weekend. I didn't mind finding a sheltered spot among the bushes, but the option of a bathroom with running water was a nice thought and worth taking advantage of. Back in the yard they had finished installing the new battery and I couldn't help but grin as I turned the key and heard the familiar roll of the engine erupting into life. Never have I been as happy to spend €85.

As I drove out of the garage, tears streamed down my face.

The road back from Mortimers Garage to Kylemore Service Station passes the most spectacular view across a lake to Kylemore Abbey. It's home to a community of Benedictine nuns who arrived in 1920 after their abbey in Belgium was destroyed in World War I. It sits into the face of Doughruagh Mountain and it is said that when it was built, back in 1868, the explosions could be heard across Connemara as they blasted the rock away. I couldn't help but wonder why the route didn't pass this way to give the runners this majestic view. I stopped the car and took a moment on the side of the road. It was time to leave the problems of this morning behind me and get back to the job in hand.

I hadn't thought about Jonathan since I left him at mile 20. I hadn't had to. Not only was Emma utterly reliable, she knew better than I did what he went through as he ran the miles. They had run hundreds of miles together in training over the years and many marathons. Emma had also been along to support Jonathan's first ultramarathon. She had seen how Jonathan often needed a few food options presented to him to hit on the one that would appeal to his taste buds. She also knew what it was to 'bonk', the not so technical term for the condition of sudden fatigue and loss of energy, and knew he had to eat 300 calories every five miles, as planned, whether he liked it or not.

The next section of the race was a nine mile stretch along Lough Inagh Valley. The landscape is barren and there isn't a single tree casting a shadow to create a spot of shelter. It was now 12.30 p.m. and Jonathan had been running for six and a half hours. The temperature had reached a high of 25°C. The course route is almost a figure of eight shape and Jonathan would be back on the same road through the valley again later that night, at about 10 p.m. by our calculations. By the time I caught up with them, Jonathan had been through the first of four official checkpoints. He was at the 30-mile point and ready for a longer break. We pulled in off the road and set up a feeding station.

Jonathan dropped himself into the foldable camping chair. In an attempt to bring down his temperature, we held the solar shower over him, fully dressed, and let the water wash over him, chair and all. I drenched his sun cap in cold water and put a wet towel over the back of his neck and shoulders so he wouldn't burn while he ate. A buffet of food was on offer. Everything from soup and sandwiches to dolmades, melon and crisps. He didn't have a huge appetite but we knew how important it was at this point that he got enough calories in. We coaxed him to try a bite of this and a spoonful of that. He managed a few spoonfuls of his recovery protein drink too. At 30 minutes, this break had lasted longer than we had planned, but he needed it. It was unnatural heat for Ireland and this was the hottest point of the day.

As Jonathan changed his clothes, Emma and I chatted about the best plan of action for the rest of the race. I was confident that the car was fixed and wouldn't break down again, but the last six hours had taken their toll. I knew I would benefit from the company. In that moment we both knew what we would do. The next stop, at mile 35, was at a church on the main Dublin–Galway–Clifden road. I could leave my car in the car park overnight. I drove on ahead. An hour later and all the supplies were packed into Emma's car and we were ready to go again. Much to Jonathan's delight, he was going to have company: Emma had decided to run too.

On the road and heading east away from Clifden, the next stop would be Peacockes Hotel, Maam Cross. This was the stretch of main road that had compelled the race organisers to insist on having a crew car behind every runner. Sitting there in Emma's car, sun shining, windows down and loud music playing, I was really enjoying this. I could see Jonathan and Emma chatting and laughing and the seven miles that we had thought would take an hour and fifty minutes in the end only took an hour and a half. Amazing what a lift company gives.

As we pulled into the hotel car park we were greeted by a smiling and waving Alan. He had arrived early and was eager to get started. We pulled around to the back of the car park and took shelter under a canopy of trees. Bathrooms were used, coffee was drunk and food was eaten. It was only after the race that I found out that Maam Cross was the spot where my paternal grandparents had met as teenagers. They had travelled to Connemara from Dublin to spend a few weeks of the summer learning Gaelic and had fallen in love.

Jonathan was ready to go. Emma, still feeling good, decided to join him for the next five mile section to Keane's Bar in Maum. Alan was happy to follow behind and I couldn't help but feel grateful for the support. I could drive there in 10 minutes and maybe snooze for the rest of the time. The sun had not stopped shining all day and temperatures along this stretch were still in the low to mid 20s. This was not the weather anyone expects in Connemara. I drove to Keane's Bar, parked the car under some trees and prepared some food for Jonathan. I couldn't get over how different the experience of crewing this race was to the other ultramarathons I had helped him with.

Up until now, Jonathan had run five ultras. Three which were on a loop, one along the quieter roads from Belfast to Dublin and one along paths and trails near and around a forest. As a supporter, the loop races are probably my favourite. You can set yourself up with a gazebo shelter, table and chair and watch the race as it takes place. You get to chat with the other supporters. There are often food trucks where you can get coffee or hot food. Your runner passes by every 40 minutes or so, depending on the length of the loop and the condition of your runner, and you can have the food prepared and ready to go and then sit back and relax in between laps. You get a great sense of the whole event and can see it unfold, cheering everyone on as the day and night pass.

The road races take a lot more work. Before setting off you have a plan where you might stop along the route to set up refreshments but that can change at a moment's notice, depending on how your runner is progressing, sometimes only needing you every five miles or so, other times needing you mile by mile. Whatever gets them through.

But this race was different and I liked it. Not only was it better having others along with me; what I loved most was that we could monitor Jonathan's condition minute by minute. I know from past experience that the mental burden of an ultramarathon can be too much sometimes. The result is the pace slows and the rest stops get longer. But being right behind him all the time, we could give him whatever he might need there and then. Right now, he had all he needed: good company.

I heard them before I saw them. Emma has a great way of chatting and distracting Jonathan from the pain of the relentless miles. The three smiling faces appeared around the corner and Alan pulled his car in beside mine. Jonathan was in great form. He had been looking forward to the next section of the race since the beginning. From here, it was about eight and a half miles to Leenaun. In three miles, Jonathan would pass the all-important halfway point. Amazingly, 12 miles done, Emma wanted to do more. I hadn't managed to sleep and I knew I would need Alan to drive behind Jonathan during the early hours of the morning, so I decided to take this stretch of road behind Emma and Jonathan. Alan headed off and I settled back into the easy pace behind the runners.

There's something lovely about slowing right down to this speed. This part of the race had a lot of ascents and in ultra-running it's common to walk the hills to conserve energy. Windows down, radio cranked up to 11, I added a soundtrack to their run. Every now and again I could see that one or the other liked the music and the pace would pick up a little or it would get them running again after a steep hill. The views from some of those peaks were incredible. There was something magical in the desolate beauty that surrounded us. As difficult as this was in the heat, it would have been miserable in the rain.

We had allowed two hours for this portion and we expected to arrive into Leenaun just before 8 p.m. This was the last town we would pass through before we got back to Clifden the next morning. On Jonathan's last 100-mile race the previous September, he had loved it when he got to one of the evening stops and I had been there with a bag of hot chips with salt and vinegar. I had also stopped and bought him chips on the Belfast 2 Dublin run too. It was a tradition, and I wasn't going to break it. I rang Alan to see if he could organise a bag of chips for about 8 p.m. It was great to have extra support crew.

Leenaun village is situated on the shore of Killary Harbour (one of only three fjords in Ireland) and was the setting for the 1990 film *The Field*. The last few miles into the village are, happily, downhill and the sun was setting over the water as we arrived. Jonathan had been struggling for a while and needed a change of socks and shoes before he could continue. We set up food and drinks on the wall looking out over the harbour. Jonathan devoured the chips and I set about removing his socks. On the Belfast 2 Dublin race he had developed blisters across the entire sole of both feet by mile 60. I took off his socks as delicately as I could, hoping it wouldn't reveal angry blisters. It didn't.

I think Jonathan would have happily sat in the camp chair all evening, but the last 45 miles were calling and he needed to get moving if he was to beat his previous times. Leenaun was the second checkpoint and, in what can only be described as relaxed fashion, one of the organising team strolled over to our picnic to take Jonathan's name and check him in. It was 8.30 p.m., 14 and a half hours since the start and, incredibly, the lead runner was on his way toward the finish line. Alastair Higgins completed the race in 14 hours, 56 minutes and 28 seconds, smashing the previous course record by almost an hour.

Emma, who had run 20 miles at this point, was going to drive to the next stop, about five miles away, and Alan and I were going to follow behind Jonathan. I expected Jonathan would take about an hour and a half on this section, which would give Emma a little break. There is a steep hill out of Leenaun and Jonathan stopped a few times to adjust his laces. I hoped the change of shoes and socks were not going to start a series of troubles. He was wearing a head torch to light the road just in front of him, and the car's headlights also added some illumination. Alan was driving so I closed my eyes and wished for sleep to come. I usually found it easy to nap, but for some reason I couldn't switch off enough. I tried counting sheep and somehow managed to manifest a mouse on the road right in front of Jonathan. The little creature brought Jonathan and the car to a dead stop. The mouse took centre stage, Jonathan's head torch the spotlight. The mouse looked at Jonathan and Jonathan looked back at the mouse. And with that, on a journey of his own through the Connemara landscape, the mouse continued across the road and disappeared into the ditch.

Emma had found respite in the car park of another church. In 12-inch-high letters the instructions *STOP AND PRAY* were painted on the wall. We obeyed half of it. Jonathan took a seat on the wall and I took out the camp stove to make some hot coffee. Emma got some tasty bits of food out for him to eat and we chatted about how much his mum and dad would enjoy knowing Jonathan was sitting at a church right at that moment.

It certainly wasn't cold but the temperature had dropped about 10 degrees since the sun went down. It was a welcome relief after a sweltering day. Emma and Alan were keeping a close eye on the time and, after the long break in Leenaun, didn't want Jonathan to delay here. The next section was the last chunk that we would all be crewing until the morning. Emma knew she would be back out running with Jonathan in the morning and had booked a B&B nearby to catch a few hours' sleep. It was almost 10.20 p.m. and Emma and Alan offered to crew him back down the nine miles of the Lough Inagh Valley. That would give me a lovely, long break. I took Alan's car and headed off to catch some zzzs. There was no need for us all to miss a night's sleep.

Weeks before, when we had our preparation call on Zoom, Jonathan had asked his three crew if we would all run the last three miles of the race with him. Not only did the Connemara 100 start with a one-mile lap of the town, but, cruelly, finished with three more laps. Jonathan had lost hours of sleep thinking about them. Knowing how difficult the final miles in previous ultramarathons had been, he thought that any gains he could scrape together might give him an advantage. How could we refuse?

I didn't know as I drove off to find sleep that Alan had decided to run the next few miles with Jonathan. This was not part of the plan. It hadn't even come up in conversation. Alan isn't a runner. He's a man who looks after his health with brisk walks and as much golf as he can squeeze in. He was a serious runner when he was younger and had completed a marathon back in the 1980s. But as someone who has run on and off over the last 10 years, I knew that level of fitness does not tend to stick around to be pulled out of thin air at the drop of a hat. Until we ditched my car, this idea had not been an option, but we now had three drivers and two cars so there was room to change the plan. Maybe Alan had always had this idea in the back of his mind and had kept it to himself. Whatever the reason, he joined Jonathan and ended up pacing him for seven miles through to the next checkpoint at mile 76.

At 1 a.m. the headlights of a car pulled in beside me on the mucky track where I was waiting. I hadn't slept but the rest had been a welcome break. Emma darted off to her B&B to get every minute of sleep she could. Alan got into the driver's seat and Jonathan took off on his own down the dark road. I was keeping a close eye on him. Having been with him on many races that ran through the night, I knew how much of a toll they took on him. The quiet road that runs down Lough Inagh Valley joins the main road and on this second pass we would be turning right towards Clifden. We were on the home stretch. What a difference 12 hours makes.

As we turned onto the main road we had a little over three and a half miles to the next stop for food. When we planned the race, we had thought rest stops every five miles would be sufficient. It had worked up until now but, as we drove behind Jonathan, Alan noticed something wasn't right. He just didn't look like he had it in him. The pep was gone. We found a safe spot and pulled in beside him.

How are you feeling? I asked through the rolled-down window. *It's about two miles to the next stop, or we can stop now.*

Now, he said without hesitation.

Alan had been right. There was something wrong.

We popped the boot of the car and got Jonathan back into the camp chair. After a day of trying to cool him down, it was time for soup. Plenty of nutrition, heat for the cold and easy to digest. The early stop meant that we would adjust the night-time plan to match and push out the next stop five miles from here.

I was glad that we were behind Jonathan when he had hit that slump. In the usual crew set-up you don't have the opportunity to react in such a prompt fashion. In other races where I've supported him, you sit at the agreed point and wait for the runner to get to you. If they hit the wall in the miles between, you don't find out until they reach you. By then it's too late. They're behind schedule, wiped out and so depleted that it can be difficult

THE VIEW FROM THE CREW CAR

to get them back on track. By being able to react immediately to Jonathan's drop in pace we sidestepped the wall.

Off the main road again, we had about nine miles to the final checkpoint in Roundstone before the last stretch to Clifden. In Ireland, this type of road is called a bhóithrín (boreen), a small country road. It had grass running down the centre, no kerb and just about enough space for one car to pass another. Watching from the car, Alan and I couldn't understand why Jonathan was keeping so close to the ditch on the side of the road. We were worried. It was 3 a.m., Jonathan had been running for 21 hours and, if he went over on his ankle, his race would be over. (Well, actually, knowing Jonathan, it wouldn't stop him but it would make the final 20 miles painfully slow.) We pulled the car up alongside him again.

Why don't you run out in the middle of the road? I said. *There's not a car in sight and we don't want you falling into the ditch.*

Without a word of response, he moved out.

The miles went slowly. Somewhere in the dead of night a car appeared in the rearview mirror. We hadn't seen one since we left the main road. They pulled up alongside us. Alan rolled down his window.

Who's the runner? they asked.

Jonathan Cairns, number 429, Alan called back.

And off they drove.

I guess that was the final checkpoint, I said and laughed.

At 4.30 a.m. we pulled into Roundstone. From here, there were about 17 miles to go. In my head it was the point where I knew Jonathan would be okay. Jonathan would crawl through cut glass to finish from there.

But he wouldn't have to do that tonight. Eighty-three miles in and he was still running.

If you haven't run or witnessed a 100-mile ultra you would be forgiven for thinking, *Well of course he would be running, why wouldn't he, it's a race, isn't it?* But ultramarathons are not like any other race. They are about as far removed from a marathon as a 5km park run is. Walking is a perfectly acceptable way to complete a 100-mile race. In fact, walking significant portions is a great technique for finishing an ultramarathon. On Jonathan's first 100-mile from Belfast to Dublin, two and a half years prior, he had run, walked and hobbled the last 42 miles after being crippled with blisters.

Jonathan needed a power nap. We had used these in races before and they really gave him the boost he needed to continue running. I set an alarm for 15 minutes, agreed in our preparation for the event. We sat him in the passenger seat of the car and put the heat on. Alan and I prepared soup, coffee and snacks for us all. Poor Jonathan thought I was messing when I roused him 15 minutes later, but it had done the trick. As he sat out on the wall where we had parked, dawn was breaking to the east over the bay and I knew the closing miles of this race were going to be different.

I love being up for the sunrise. On ultramarathon race days the sunrise changes everything. The miles in the dark must be exhausting for the runner. Every step, eyes straining to see where you're running with just the faint light of the head torch to light the ground in front of you.

By the time we left Roundstone it was 5 a.m. With the end in sight we started to do the calculations. For this race, the cut-off was 30 hours after the start, 12 noon on Sunday. We had no doubt Jonathan would finish, but would he beat his previous best of 28 hours and 45 minutes? He needed to get in before 10.45 a.m. to beat his previous record. That gave him 5 hours and 45 minutes to complete 17 miles or a little over 20 minutes a mile. Twenty minutes a mile was absolutely possible; we just needed to make sure he didn't delay on the rest stops.

A few miles outside Roundstone a familiar car came towards us. It was Emma and she was all smiles. She had had her coffee. She pulled in behind us and we travelled in convoy to the next rest stop. It was breakfast time and Jonathan and I had planned for this. We knew from the race the year before that morning rituals gave Jonathan a huge lift. I set the solar shower up on the highest object I could find, a gatepost. Standing there, in only his shorts, Jonathan soaked under the water, letting the sweat, dust and dirt of the last 24 hours run off him. A full change of clothes, coffee, a sausage sandwich, teeth brushed and he was off on what we were all treating as the final leg.

We sent Alan 10 miles down the road to mile 95. After driving through the night, it was a well-earned break for him. I sat in Emma's car and we chatted about the hours since she'd left. She hadn't had much sleep in the time between. You take on a lot of responsibility in a support role and it's hard to switch off. I was familiar with the worries that had been running through her mind when she lay down to rest:

What if I sleep through my alarm? What if they have a problem with their car and need me? I'm not sure my phone is charging, I should check it again. Will Jonathan eat enough calories at the breaks? I hope he hasn't any blisters...

Happy to be back out with Jonathan, she turned to me and asked if I was rested enough to drive again.

Absolutely, I said without thinking. In fact, I had no idea if I was rested or not. I was running on adrenaline and I knew that I would be wide awake until Jonathan crossed the finish line. Emma wanted to run again and I was delighted. I knew there was nothing he would like more than to have someone out running with him.

I took up the familiar position behind my husband and his 'running wife', as Emma was known in our house. I turned on the radio and got a giggle when ABBA's *The Winner Takes It All* came on. Jonathan's favourite movie (I'm sure he won't mind me saying) is *Mamma Mia*! I turned the volume right up and I imagine the residents of the usually quiet Ballyconneely village were perplexed as to why they were being awoken so early on a Sunday morning by the Swedish quartet. Jonathan was so keenly focused on the finish line that he sacrificed his food break at mile 90 and ran on to Alan and mile 95. There was no holding him back. He was hungry for the finish line.

At 8.30 a.m. we pulled into the car park where Alan was waiting. After 26 and a half hours of crawling along behind the runners, I was looking forward to getting out of the car. I had no doubt at this point that Jonathan would beat his previous time – the question now was by how much?

I'd like to run to Clifden with Jonathan, Alan said.

We were about two miles from the town and then all that was left were the three laps of the town.

Okay, I said. *I'll take your car, Emma can crew you and I'll see you in Clifden for the final three miles.*

I gave Jonathan a kiss and headed for the finish.

Arriving into Clifden I found a parking spot and changed into my running gear on the street. Jonathan and Alan weren't far behind. By the time I walked a few hundred metres back out of the town I could see the familiar shape of the two of them making their way up the final hill into the town, with Emma minding their backs. Once I joined them, Emma overtook and high-tailed it into town to park her car.

This was it. The moment Jonathan had dreamed about. Having his crew run the last three miles with him. I'm ashamed to admit that I struggled through those miles. I've never found running easy, never getting to that point where it all becomes effortless, blissful, meditative. For my first mile-long lap I spent my time wondering if it would be okay if I ran this first lap, then sat out the second lap and then joined in again for the final lap. Then I told myself to cop on and suck it up. Jonathan had just run 97 miles. Wasn't he suffering these miles too? He didn't look it. Not from where I was anyway. Behind him, car or no car, that was my place this weekend.

Alan was the pacer for us all now. He was keeping an eye on the clock each time we crossed the finish line. It's disconcerting to cross the finish line several times before you actually *cross* the finish line. He knew exactly what was needed to get Jonathan in more than one hour faster than his previous best and coached us all through those last few miles. As we rounded the final turn toward the finish we could see the clock. Jonathan crossed the line in the time of 27 hours and 38 minutes. A full hour and seven minutes faster than the race a year earlier. And this time in extraordinary conditions.

The moments that follow the end of a race are filled with emotion. Some people laugh. I cry. They're happy tears. They're a way for everything that I have used to hold it all together to be released.

Medal in hand, we found ourselves a cafe and ordered everything on the menu. Exhausted, we struggled through breakfast until the food and coffee took effect. It wasn't long before we were back in the cars and on the road to pick up our car where we had left it on Saturday afternoon in front of the church. From there, Alan and Emma faced the long drive back to Dublin. Jonathan and I had taken the week off work and were looking forward to a leisurely three-day road trip down the west coast of Ireland before spending a few days, with our feet up, with Jonathan's family who live in beautiful West Cork.

Arriving at the church car park I was walloped with exhaustion. I knew I would be the driver for the next few days and there was no way I could safely continue without a sleep. The sun was beaming down so I pulled the duvet out of the car and spread it out on the grass under a tree in the churchyard and lay down with Jonathan to sleep.

Back in Dublin a week later and the thank you cards came out. I had two amazing teammates and a guardian angel in Clifden I had to thank.

When he's not running ultramarathons, Jonathan spends his days working in a busy Dublin hospital. It's not work that he loves but he took it on when the global financial crash in 2008 destroyed his business and we needed a second source of income. Over the years, Jonathan has cared for people in their final months, weeks and days and, while it's clear that he has given them great comfort, I think the gift they have given him far outweighs that.

He never takes his health for granted. When he wakes up feeling well, he honours the day by getting up and making the most of it. When he's not working, he writes or he runs. He sits back to read a book and drink a coffee or chats with his son Jem about the Irish team selection for the upcoming rugby match. He meets his friend Dylan and cycles up a mountain or meets his nephew Isaac, and his friends, to leap off the rocks into the freezing Irish Sea. He lives every day.

He's familiar with pain. Jonathan has three kids but circumstances have separated him from his two gorgeous daughters and that breaks his heart. And right now, in 2020, he's watching his eldest sister live through the terrifying ordeal of motor neuron disease. Not being able to be with her due to COVID-19 restrictions make that even more difficult.

I'm among the many who have, on occasion, asked Jonathan why he chooses to undertake these extreme races. The answer he always gives is, *Because I can*. It's an extraordinary approach to life and one that I hope will rub off on me someday.

Appendices

MY RECIPES

henever I go to a party where I bring food, I never mention that it is gluten-free. On being told a dish is gluten-free, most people avoid it as if the cat has done something on it. The general reaction tends to be that it must taste terrible if the gluten is taken out of it. Depending where you go, it can be similar with a vegetarian dish. I find that if I suffer from a slight bout of confusion when asked what's in something, it has a good chance of being devoured.

Ten years ago as a vegetarian coeliac, I never got invited anywhere unless inviting me was unavoidable. Even then I usually got a last-minute text saying, *Bring something you can eat.* Now everything has changed, including myself.

Back in the day, an Irish dinner was never recognised as a dinner unless it had meat and two vegetables. One of the vegetables was usually potatoes, the other overcooked to the point of being tasteless. To give flavour we added table salt and gravy, which was a brown sauce mixed with all the fat of the meat (just in case you had any over-functioning arteries that need slowing down), wheat flour to thicken it and usually a stock cube to add extra salt. And it was poured over everything. Most compliments on the dinner depended on the gravy. It was probably the exact opposite to what any health-conscious human might eat, let alone a vegan coeliac.

Happily, we have moved along and now recognise that some things like smoking and old-fashioned meals are bad for us and other things like fresh fruit and vegetables are good for us. Fresh foods are now readily available and almost every man, woman and child recognises good food from bad. Processed foods with sugar and salt are known to be not so good. Some of us think poor health is something that happens to us. In certain cases this is true, of course, but those who don't take any responsibility for their own health tend to eat poorly. Anyone who takes 100% responsibility for their own health tends to take notice of what they put on their plate at mealtimes.

As a runner, I continuously search for a healthy, energetic lifestyle. It's been a long, hard road but very rewarding and possibly life-saving. To mix daily exercise with energy-giving, tasty food is now the daily quest. For me, one of the benefits of eating less meat is having more energy and strength. The foods I eat are typical vegan foods and consist of grains, legumes, nuts and seeds, vegetables and fruits.

As part of my ongoing upkeep, I use *Dr Greger's Daily Dozen* (from his book *How Not to Die*) as a health guide. If I can incorporate all or most of these into my day, I know I am doing well.

Beans	Berries	Other Fruits	Cruciferous Vegetables
Servings: 3 per day	Servings: 1 per day	Servings: 3 per day	Servings: 1 per day
e.g. ½ c. cooked beans, ¼ c. hummus	e.g. ½ c. fresh or frozen, ¼ c. dried	e.g. 1 medium fruit, ¼ c. dried fruit	e.g. ½ c. chopped, 1 tbsp horseradish
Greens	**Other Vegetables**	**Flaxseed**	**Nuts and Seeds**
Servings: 2 per day	Servings: 2 per day	Servings: 1 per day	Servings: 1 per day
e.g. 1 c. raw, ½ c. cooked	e.g. ½ c. nonleafy vegetables	e.g. 1 tbsp ground	e.g. ¼ c. nuts, 2 tbsp nut butter
Herbs and Spices	**Whole Grains**	**Beverages**	**Exercise**
Servings: 1 per day	Servings: 3 per day	Servings: 60 oz per day	Servings: Once per day
e.g. ¼ tsp turmeric	e.g. ½ c. hot cereal, 1 slice of bread	e.g. Water, green tea, hibiscus tea	e.g. 90 min. moderate or 40 min. vigorous

Vitamin B12

At least 2,000 mcg (µg) cyanocobalamin once each week (or at least 50 mcg daily), ideally as a chewable, sublingual, or liquid supplement taken on an empty stomach.

All year round I take a few supplements. When the training gets tough, if I start to feel the effects of so much exercise, I pay a visit to my local health food shop. Otherwise, on a regular day I take vitamin C to keep my immune system firing on all cylinders, magnesium to support bone health, improve my digestion and help me sleep, B12 as I do not eat meat and want to be sure I don't suffer from tiredness or foggy brain, B complex for nerve function and energy levels, and vitamin D for maintaining my immune system and my bones and muscles.

I don't think I'd be running ultramarathons had I not looked at my food. At every stage along the way, paying attention has paid off. But putting recipes in a paperback feels a little strange. The lack of mouth-watering, instagrammable food photos is obvious. However, I know what it's like to be undertaking the mammoth task of running your first ultramarathon and searching for all the pieces of the puzzle that will help you achieve that goal. The following pages contain the recipes that are mentioned throughout the book and are our regular go-to meals at home. I hope they inspire you to look at what you're eating to help fuel you or aid your recovery.

In *The Plant-Based Runner*, I included recipes that had helped me transition to eating plant-based foods. Changing my diet and substituting meals and snacks with tasty alternatives took a lot of work. If you're looking to include more plant-based and gluten-free foods in your diet, *The Plant Based-Runner* is a good place to start.

Recipes not included here that you'll find in *The Plant-Based Runner*:

- ▶ Granola
- ▶ Oat Pancakes
- ▶ Sweet Potato & Chestnut Mushroom Soup
- ▶ Pea & Parsley Soup
- ▶ Chickpea & Butternut Squash Salad
- ▶ Kale, Sprouted Beans & Goji Salad
- ▶ Beetroot with Walnut & Cumin
- ▶ Roast Butternut Squash & Pineapple Massaman Curry
- ▶ Pumpkin Curry with Chickpeas
- ▶ Puy Lentil & Coriander Pesto Bake with Sweet Potato Mash

- ▶ Spicy Lentil & Aubergine Pasta
- ▶ Vegetable Biryani
- ▶ Refried Beans Foldover
- ▶ Chilli & Avocado Toast
- ▶ Almond Butter & Banana Toast
- ▶ Stuffed Savoury Chickpea Wraps
- ▶ Savoury Indian Pancakes
- ▶ Cumin-Spiced Sweet Potato Wedges
- ▶ Brazil Nut Pesto
- ▶ Guacamole
- ▶ Cambodian Wedding Dip
- ▶ Innocent Millionaire's Shortbread
- ▶ Avocado Chocolate Mousse Cake
- ▶ Granola Bars
- ▶ Protein Grenades

Breakfasts

Pimped Up Toast and Peanut Butter

This is the quickest breakfast option on the list here and works as a snack anytime too. It's regularly what I would eat before a run to get up and out the door.

Base

If bread is your preference, try and choose something with less squish. The squishier the bread, the more likely it is to be filled with ingredients that spike your blood sugar. You're looking for a slower release of energy to sustain you over a longer period of time, whether that's out running, or remote working and homeschooling the kids. Since I'm a coeliac, the majority of store-bought breads are not an option for me. Fiona and I ditched white bread as one of our very first steps into a healthier lifestyle and so our version of peanut butter on toast may often be peanut butter on oatcakes, corn cakes, buckwheat bread or homemade bread. Toasted bread will give a nice warm base which will soften the peanut butter.

(Pea)nut Butter Topping

So this is where it gets interesting. If you're using peanut butter, the best option is one made with 100% peanuts, zero palm oil and zero sugar or sugar substitutes. However you're not limited to peanut butter and it's worth trying out some of the nut butter alternatives made with almonds, cashews or hazelnuts or the seed butters like tahini (sesame), pumpkin and sunflower. Typically the alternatives are more expensive than peanut butter, but they make for a lovely change of flavour.

Pimp It Up Toppings

Salt is the easiest way to pimp this up. (Only add salt if you are using a 100% nut butter with no added salt). A little goes a long way and a tiny pinch of sea salt sprinkled on top or a crunch of Himalayan salt is plenty. Bear in mind, most people get more sodium than they need in their diets these days. Processed food is loaded with salt and it can be a constant struggle to keep it to a minimum. So I keep an eye on the salt we add to the foods we make at home.

If you'd rather go sweet, try adding a drizzle of honey/maple/agave. Or you might like to try what I do and add a sprinkle of salt to the sweet.

Banana is the next topping to try. Mash it, slice it, just lay it on top. Whatever floats your boat.

Apple and peanut butter are a great combination. Peanut butter on apple slices are a mid-race staple when I'm running ultras. So try some thinly sliced apple on top. A sprinkle of cinnamon on this will work too.

If you're looking for something more substantial, why not try a satay-inspired sandwich or open sandwich (one slice of bread). We do this with tofu. Two hundred grams of tofu serves two people comfortably.

Ingredients:
- 1 block of tofu (firm or extra firm). The size of the tofu will vary by brand. Adjust marinade depending on how much tofu you have.
- enough bread for your chosen serving style.

Marinade (for 200 g tofu):
- 3 tbsp smooth peanut butter
- 1 tbsp soy sauce or tamari (for gluten-free diets)
- 1 tbsp freshly squeezed lime juice
- 1 tsp maple syrup
- 1 clove crushed garlic
- 1 tsp freshly grated ginger

Toppings:
- sliced cucumbers
- shredded carrots
- chopped spring onions
- drizzle of sweet or hot chilli sauce

Method:

- Mix all the marinade ingredients in a bowl. Add a splash of water or warm it in a saucepan if it is too thick to stir.
- Cut the tofu into thick slices (approx. ½ cm).
- Cover all sides of the tofu slices in the marinade and allow to sit for 20 minutes in the sauce.
- Heat the oven to 180°C. Place the tofu on greaseproof paper in a baking dish, and bake for 25 minutes. Keep any of the remaining marinade, left behind from the tofu, to use during the baking.
- After 15 minutes, turn the tofu and drizzle any of the leftover marinade on top.
- Make up your sandwich with sliced cucumbers, shredded carrots, chopped spring onions and drizzle with sweet or hot chilli sauce.

Fresh Fruit Salad with Seeds

Like a lot of the things I concoct, I make do with what I have on hand, which tends to be what's at its ripest when I'm doing the weekly shop. As a result, I often don't follow a recipe per se, but rather have some guidelines for what I'm looking to achieve. And when it comes to my fruit salad, I'm looking primarily for antioxidants. Something to combat the oxidative stress the body undergoes from too many free radicals, generated from running (and living life).

While herbs and spices pack the greatest antioxidant punch, berries come in second and average 10 times more antioxidants than other fruits and vegetables. I always have blueberries in my fridge and I regularly eat them straight from the pot by the handful. They are a runner's best friend. You may have heard the phrase 'Eat the Rainbow' and that's what I aim for here.

Serves 2

Ingredients:

- 1 mango
- ⅓ pineapple
- 2 cups chopped melon (cantaloupe, honeydew or watermelon all work well)
- 1 or 2 kiwifruit
- 2 handfuls berries
- juice of ½ a lemon

Toppings:

- 2 tbsp seeds (choose from whatever you have; pumpkin, sunflower, chia, sesame or flaxseed all work)
- 1 tbsp goji berries
- 1 tbsp cacao nibs

Method:

- Chop the mango, pineapple, melon and kiwifruit into bite-sized pieces. Add them all to a large bowl along with the berries.
- Squeeze the juice of ½ a lemon over the fruit and mix through.
- If preparing the night before, split the fruit between two containers with airtight lids. Sprinkle the seeds, goji and cacao nibs over both and cover with lid.

Overnight Oats

Oats are my favourite go-to food. They go in my recovery drinks and energy bars and I use them to make bread. As long as there are oats in the cupboard, everything will be okay. As a coeliac I have to buy gluten-free porridge oats. Although oats are naturally gluten-free, they are regularly processed in machines that deal with other grains and cross-contamination occurs. Something you also need to look out for in oat milk.

As with all my recipes, you'll see a theme emerging. Unlike baking, which requires precision to achieve the result you are looking for, it's pretty hard to get this wrong. Use what you like and what you have to hand.

Serves 2

Ingredients:

- 1 cup oats
- 2 cups water or milk

Toppings:

- 1 cup fresh fruit or ⅓ cup dried fruit. I tend to pick just one fruit to minimise the quick-release sugars. Options include berries, sliced banana or grated apple or, if using dry fruit, consider goji berries, raisins, sultanas, chopped dates or apricots.
- 4 tbsp seeds (pumpkin, sunflower, chia, sesame or flaxseed all work)
- 4 tbsp nuts (almonds, pecans, walnuts, hazelnuts or whatever you have to hand)
- 2 tbsp cacao nibs
- Most people have their favourite spices. Cinnamon, vanilla, nutmeg or fresh grated ginger work well here. If you have spiced poached pears, they make an amazing topping combining both the fruit and spice elements.

Method:

- As the name suggests, this is one you prepare the night before. I use two large 500 ml jars and put half the ingredients into each. You can also just put it all in one bowl and cover with a cloth.
- Put half the oats in each jar and add the liquid of choice.
- If you're adding grated apple and/or dried fruit, mix them through the oats and milk so they can soak overnight. Other fruit can just be added as a layer on top.
- You can add the rest of the toppings now and let them sit on top, or pop them in a small container and just add them when you are ready to eat.
- Store in the fridge.

Green Vegetable Smoothie

This has been part of my life for over 10 years. It was the very first step Fiona and I took in adding one daily healthy element to our lives. It has certainly changed over the years from where we first started. My body appreciates the nutrition and, if I skip a day or feel low, it starts to crave a smoothie.

In the beginning, we were on the juice-only bus. We went through quite a number of juicers over the years as they take quite a beating, masticating the fruits and veggies that come down the chute. But our opinion on juices versus smoothies slowly changed, mainly because of the huge amount of waste in juicing. (If you haven't made a juice before, the machine 'chews up' the produce and separates the juice from the fibre, leaving you with one container of liquid and another of dry shredded fibre.)

We buy the best fruit and vegetables we can and local and organic where possible. Because of this, we hate to see so much of that lovely organic produce going in the compost bin. So at the moment we make smoothies and get all the goodness in one. That's not to say that green vegetable juices don't have a role to play in health. They are packed with easy-to-absorb nutrients and are light and easy to drink.

What follows is another of my 'whatever is fresh and green gets thrown in' recipes. A few tips if you're new to vegetable smoothies.

1. If your taste buds are not used to drinking savoury drinks, you may find the recipe below hard to swallow. I did when I started. The easiest thing to do is start out by adding a slice of pineapple (skin and core removed) or an apple (core removed) to sweeten it and reduce this over time until you don't miss the sweetness.

2. Once the produce has been blended, the nutrients degrade quickly (think of how an avocado turns brown once exposed to air), but we have been making our smoothies the night before for years and have found that works well for us. Once it's made, we decant it into smaller glass bottles filled right to the top to minimise the air in the bottle, sealed tightly and stored in the fridge.

3. If you're using organic produce you can leave the skins on (unwaxed) lemons and limes.

We have a Vitamix blender with a 2-litre jug and always make a full jug. Adjust quantities to suit your blender.

Makes 4 large 500 ml portions

Ingredients:
- ⅓ cucumber
- ⅓ courgette
- 2 large handfuls leaves like spinach or kale (with kale I remove the tougher stems)
- ½–1 lemon or lime (seeds and stem end removed, skin left on if organic and unwaxed)
- ½–1 avocado (stone and skin removed)
- 3 or 4 sticks celery
- generous slice of fennel
- big knob of ginger
- big piece turmeric root
- 1 handful of fresh parsley or coriander
- water as needed to fill remainder of jug

Other Suitable Ingredients:
- 1 tbsp spirulina or chlorella powder
- 1 tbsp of lecithin granules
- 1 scoop protein powder (avoid flavoured powders for this recipe)

Method:
- Chop the courgette, cucumber, lemon/lime, avocado, celery, fennel, ginger and turmeric and add to the blender jug.
- Throw in the spinach leaves and herbs.
- Add any other dry powdered ingredients.
- The ingredients should fill about three-quarters of the jug.

Once you start blending they will drop down. To start blending, add about 300 ml water, or just enough to get the mix going. The blender I use is very powerful and I blend it with a small amount of water for about 30 seconds on the lowest setting. I then add enough water to fill the jug to the 2-litre mark and slowly increase the speed until I reach full power. Finally, I blend at full speed for another 30 seconds.

▫ You want a smooth, pourable liquid. If it's too thick, just fill your bottles to about three-quarters full and top up with water and shake.

Light Meals

Vegan Sushi

I dodged sushi for many years due to the raw fish element which never appealed to me. It's only in recent years that I realised that sushi doesn't have to have fish. Vegan sushi is amazing and, with a little bit of practice, is a really tasty treat to make at home.

This recipe is for a sushi roll, Futomaki (Maki Sushi). It's a traditional, chunky roll of sushi filled with colourful ingredients.

Before you have a go at making your own sushi, I would say that a sushi rolling mat is pretty much an essential. I know there are ways to roll the sushi with a towel but I tried, and failed, and then got a mat and, hey presto, sushi happened! I would also recommend watching a couple of videos to see exactly what technique is used to get everything tightly rolled up.

It's also important to use *sushi* rice and not any other types of rice. It's the only time I eat white rice. I haven't figured out a way to make it with brown rice yet.

There is a lot of fuss about making sushi rice online. Everywhere I looked I was reminded time and again to only use a wooden spoon when working with the cooked rice. A metal spoon or bowl could react with the vinegar in the seasoning. I haven't had any difficulty with the method below, but then I'm no expert and who knows if it tastes like it should. All I know is, I love it.

Serves 3 (as a lighter bite)

Ingredients:
Sushi:
- 1 cup sushi rice
- 1 ¼ cups water

Rice Seasoning:
- 2 ½ tbsp rice vinegar
- ½ tbsp maple syrup
- ½ tsp salt

Fillings:
- avocado
- cucumber
- spring onions
- red pepper
- carrot

For Wrapping Sushi Rolls:
- ¼ cup water (for dipping fingers)
- 2 tsp rice vinegar (for dipping fingers)
- 6 sheets nori (seaweed)

To Serve:
- wasabi
- soy sauce or tamari (for gluten-free diets)

Method:
- Apart from your saucepan, do not use any metal bowls or utensils when working with the cooked rice.
- Rinse the rice thoroughly, until the water runs clear. It can take multiple washes before all the surface starch is removed.
- Place the rice in your cooking pot, add the water and turn the heat up high.
- You need to watch the rice at first, stirring every minute, until the water comes to the boil.
- Once the water is boiling, reduce the heat to a simmer and cover the pot.
- Set a timer for six minutes.
- While the rice is cooking, mix the seasoning ingredients and set aside.
- After six minutes, check the rice. If all the water has been absorbed, the rice is done. If there is still some water, cover and check again every minute until it is cooked.
- Gently move the rice from the pot to a large dish and spread it out.

- Add about half the seasoning to the rice and stir through gently. Taste and add the remaining seasoning, to suit your palate.

- You need to wait for the rice to cool. The more you are able to spread out the rice, the quicker it will cool.

- While the rice is cooling, prepare your fillings by cutting them into narrow strips and batons.

- Prepare your area by placing all your fillings, your bamboo rolling mat, the cooled rice, the nori sheets and a small bowl with the water and vinegar for dipping your fingers on the counter in front of you. Dip your fingers in the vinegar water before and during working with the rice. It will help keep your fingers clean and prevent the rice from sticking.

- The nori sheet has two sides. One side is flat and one has slight ridges (like the marks the string on the bamboo rolling mat would leave). Begin by laying a sheet of nori on the bamboo rolling mat, ridges facing up.

- Take a handful of rice, about the size of a tennis ball, and place it in the centre of the nori. Move the rice around gently with your fingertips, without pressing it too hard. The aim is to spread the rice out evenly over the sheet, leaving about one centimetre on the edge furthest away from you.

- Once you have an even layer of rice, start adding your fillings along the edge nearest you, starting about one centimetre in. The fillings run left to right and each filling should spread across the width of the rice. For example, select pieces of cucumber that, when placed end-to-end, fit in a single row across the rice. Now take your second filling and repeat, keeping the fillings as close together as possible. Repeat until you have four or five fillings in a row across the rice. You do not want to cover all the rice with fillings, just a small area on the side nearest you.

- Now, using your fingers to keep the fillings in place, lift the bamboo mat on the side closest to you with your thumbs. Use the mat to help you roll the nori sheet and rice like a Swiss roll, without getting the bamboo mat caught up. The mat should stay on the outside at all times. Roll it as tight as you can and stop when you get to the end of the rice. Keeping everything in place with one hand, dip the thumb of your other hand into the vinegar water and run your damp thumb across the final exposed edge of the nori. Complete the roll by pressing gently to stick the damp nori to the outside of the roll.

- When finished, the roll should be nice and tight with a colourful centre.
- You can eat the roll whole, like a burrito, or cut into fat slices. A clean, wet knife will cut the sushi easier.
- I serve my vegan sushi with tamari and wasabi for dipping.

Sweet Potato and Coconut Soup

This would be my equivalent to ice cream. I don't like ice cream so when I go through a break-up I sit on the couch watching *Mamma Mia!* drinking this soup. That's not true, but it could be. Soup is a great evening meal for me. I like to eat the majority of my calories earlier in the day and this is really easy for me to digest which helps with getting a good night's sleep. This soup, or a variation of it, is also something I eat during races.

The vegetables can be changed to suit what you have to hand, just keep the volume of vegetables to liquid about the same and you can't really go wrong (approx. 1 kg of vegetables to 1 ½ litres of liquid).

Serves 4

Ingredients:
- coconut oil for frying
- 2 onions, diced
- 500 g sweet potatoes, cut into chunks
- 300 g carrots, cut into chunks
- 2 garlic cloves, minced

- large knob ginger, grated
- piece turmeric root, grated (grating the turmeric may stain your fingers)
- 1 tsp cumin
- 1 tsp coriander
- 1 L hot vegetable stock
- 400 ml coconut milk
- salt & pepper to taste

Method:

- Place a knob of coconut oil in a large pot on a medium heat and add the onions. Sauté for three minutes and add the carrots. Reduce the heat, cover and cook for about five minutes, stirring occasionally.
- Add the sweet potatoes, garlic, ginger, turmeric, cumin and coriander and mix until the vegetables and spices are well combined. Cook for a minute or two.
- Pour in the hot stock and coconut milk, mix well and turn up the heat. Bring the soup to boil before reducing the heat to a simmer. Cover and cook for 15 minutes.
- Remove from the heat and blend to preferred consistency (a stick blender is the easiest way to do this). Season with salt and pepper to taste.

Substantial Meals

Lentil and Vegetable Shepherdless Pie

One of my favourite meals. Nutritious, wholesome and loved by the kids.

There are a few recipes we go back to again and again (and again). This is one of them. We discovered it when we first went vegan and were looking for things that were familiar. It is very forgiving.

Want to swap rosemary for thyme? Go for it. Want to have ordinary potato mash on top, rather than sweet potato? Do it. Just want the lentil base with a salad or other roast veg on the side? Yum, send me an invite and I'll be round for dinner.

The recipe below will serve six to eight people. For us that means we can have dinner and lunch and still have enough left over to freeze a few portions for when we're stuck for a meal.

Serves 6–8

Ingredients:
- 2 onions, diced
- 2 cloves of garlic, minced
- 6 mushrooms, sliced
- 400 g dried French or Puy lentils
- 1 L hot vegetable stock
- 2 carrots, chopped
- 100 g frozen peas
- coconut oil for cooking
- 1 bay leaf
- a few sprigs of fresh thyme (or 1 tsp dried)
- 1 tbsp soy sauce or tamari (for gluten-free diets)
- 1 tbsp balsamic vinegar
- 1 tbsp tomato puree
- salt & pepper to taste

Topping:
- 1 kg potatoes or sweet potatoes (a mix of both works well too)

- 2 tbsp Dijon mustard
- large knob vegan butter
- a good splash of plant-based milk (oat or soya work best as they are savoury and don't carry much flavour; remember to check the oat milk is gluten-free if serving someone with a gluten intolerance)
- salt & pepper to taste

Method:

- The dried lentils need a really good rinse before cooking. Rinse until the water runs clear and keep an eye out for tiny stones which you'll occasionally find among the lentils. You want to weed these out before you cook the lentils or you could crack a tooth.
- Place a knob of coconut oil in a large pot on a medium heat and add the onions. Sauté for three minutes and add the garlic. Cook for another minute before adding the mushrooms. Keep the heat medium or raise it slightly, until the mushrooms have browned and released all their liquid.
- Add the rinsed and drained lentils to the pot along with a litre of hot stock. Put the bay leaf, thyme, tamari, balsamic vinegar and tomato puree in now too. Turn up the heat, stirring occasionally until it comes to the boil. Reduce heat to a simmer and cover.
- The lentils will take about 40 minutes to cook. After 25 minutes, add the carrots, stir and cover. With three minutes to go, add the peas, stir and cover.
- While the lentils are cooking, prepare the potato mash topping.
- Most people peel potatoes and sweet potatoes when making mash, but since the skin is full of nutrition, I leave them on (and yes, it's less work too). Chop the potatoes into large evenly sized pieces. Add them to a pot of boiling water and

simmer for about 15 minutes. They're ready when you can stick a fork or knife easily into the potato. Drain thoroughly and put the pot back on the cooker with no heat below. Put a clean tea towel or a few squares of kitchen paper over the potatoes to absorb the steam. After a few minutes remove the towel. The potatoes should be nice and dry and fluffy at the edges.

▫ Mash the potatoes, adding a large knob of vegan butter, the mustard and a splash of plant-based milk. The skin will not break up fully, but that's okay. Season to taste.

▫ Preheat the oven to 200°C.

▫ Once the lentils are ready, taste and season with salt and pepper, if needed. Put them in a large baking dish. Spoon the mash on top and spread it evenly across the top using a fork. Put the dish in the oven for about 20–25 minutes until the top is lightly browned.

Pad Thai with Tofu and Vegetables

I discovered this dish when my son Jem ordered it from our local Thai takeaway. One taste and I was hooked. Fiona did what she does and searched out a simple alternative and made it at home. Traditional pad thai would include eggs, shrimp, dried shrimp and fish sauce. We've left all these out. Does it taste just like traditional pad thai? I don't know. Does it hit the spot? Definitely. I probably like this a little too much and find the rice noodles very easy to digest. I always make enough for dinner along with a couple of portions to cover lunch the next day.

Serves 4

Ingredients:
▫ rice noodles for four
For the Stir-Fry:
▫ coconut oil for stir-fry
▫ 1 tbsp soy sauce or tamari (for gluten-free diets), for cooking

the mushrooms

- 200 g firm tofu, drained, dried and cubed
- 200 g mushrooms, sliced
- 4 spring onions, cut into bite-sized, long thin strips
- 2 cloves garlic, minced
- 100 g carrots, spiralised or cut into long thin strips
- 100 g bean sprouts

Sauce:

- ½ cup peanut butter (crunchy or smooth works, I choose one made from 100% peanuts)
- 2 tbsp soy sauce or tamari (for gluten-free diets)
- 1 tbsp maple syrup
- juice of ½ a lime

To Serve:

- 60 g roasted unsalted peanuts, crushed
- lime wedges
- a handful of fresh coriander, roughly chopped (including stems)

Method:

- Cook the rice noodles, following the instructions on the packet. For mine they just sit in a bowl of boiled water for five minutes and then I run them under cold water to stop them cooking. They go back into the stir-fry at the end which heats them back up again.
- Prepare the sauce by adding all the ingredients to a bowl and whisk well. Have a taste and adjust sweet or savoury notes by adding more soy sauce/tamari or maple.
- Have all your stir-fry ingredients prepped as this one is quick to make.
- Heat a large wok or pan over a medium heat. Place a knob of coconut oil in the pan and add the tofu. Turn it every couple of minutes until the tofu is brown on all sides. Set aside.

- Now add the mushrooms to the pan along with a tablespoon of soy sauce/tamari. The mushrooms don't need any oil and adding a little tamari will get all the nice bits of flavour left behind by the tofu off the pan and onto the mushrooms. Once the mushrooms have browned, and the liquid they released has evaporated, you can set them aside with the tofu.
- Place another knob of coconut oil in the pan and add the spring onions, garlic, carrots and bean sprouts and toss for a minute or two. Add back in the tofu and mushrooms and mix everything well.
- Add the cooked, drained rice noodles and toss everything together gently.
- Pour the sauce over the pan and make sure it covers everything well. Give everything one last toss before serving straight into bowls.
- Garnish with crushed peanuts, a sprinkle of chopped coriander and a wedge of lime on the side.

Quick Vegetables with Brown Rice

When I'm tired or have very little time, I make this fast nutritious meal. I don't really mind what vegetables go in and use whatever we have in the fridge at the time of cooking. This works really well with tofu, beans or chickpeas added and occasionally I'll swap the tamari for a tin of coconut milk or chopped tomatoes for variety. I serve this with brown rice.

Serves 2

Ingredients:
- coconut oil for frying
- 400 g tofu or tin of butter beans or chickpeas
- 2 cloves garlic, minced
- 2–3 leeks, sliced
- 100 g mushrooms, sliced
- 1 red pepper, bite-sized pieces

- □ 100 g baby broccoli
- □ 50 g frozen peas
- □ 3 tbsp soy sauce or tamari (for gluten-free diets)
- □ brown rice for two

Method:

- □ Put the brown rice on to cook before you start the vegetables as the rice will probably take longer to cook. Follow the instructions on the packet.
- □ Place a knob of coconut oil in a large wok or frying pan over a medium heat.
- □ If using tofu, cut into bite-sized pieces and add this to the pan first, browning on all sides. Remove from the pan and set aside.
- □ Add the mushrooms, turn up the heat and let them brown and release their liquid. Let the liquid evaporate before reducing the heat to medium again.
- □ Add a little more oil to the pan, along with the garlic and leeks and cook for three to five minutes until softened.
- □ Add the remaining veg to the pan and keep everything moving, so it cooks evenly.
- □ Add the tofu back into the pan along with the tamari and mix well. If you're using a tin of butter beans or chickpeas instead of tofu, drain them first and add to the pan at this point too.
- □ I like my vegetables to have a nice bite, so I don't cook them for long.
- □ Serve with brown rice.

The Everything Salad

As salad lovers, we eat this a lot. We're lucky enough to have locally grown salad leaves available to us weekly and we stock up at our local market in Ballydehob every Wednesday. If I'm having this as my main meal, which I eat at lunchtime, I serve it with a baked potato or sweet potato and add grilled tofu. In the evening I pair it with soup. Being generous with all the gorgeous toppings, and serving it in a large flat salad dish, makes it as appealing to the eyes as it is to the tastebuds. Fiona prepares the salad dressing in our house and I've included her recipe below.

Serves 2 generously

Ingredients:

- enough seeds to roughly cover the base of a frying pan (sunflower, sesame, pumpkin, flaxseed)
- sea salt
- 2–3 handfuls rocket
- 2–3 handfuls mixed green leaves
- 2–3 spring onions, sliced
- 1 avocado, bite-sized pieces
- ½–1 red pepper, bite-sized pieces
- a scattering of olives (I love small, dark kalamata olives in salad)
- a small handful of goji berries

Dressing:

- 3 tbsp oil (olive, pumpkin, hazelnut are all lovely)
- 1 tbsp vinegar (apple cider or balsamic)
- juice of ½ a lemon
- 1 tsp tahini
- ½ tsp maple
- 1 clove garlic, crushed
- ½ tsp turmeric powder
- salt & pepper to taste

Method:

- Heat the seeds on a hot dry pan, tossing regularly. Remove from the heat once you start to smell them toasting and they have turned slightly brown. Add a generous sprinkle of sea salt, and set aside.

- Place the leaves in the serving dish and arrange all the other salad ingredients. Then top with the toasted seeds.
- Add all the dressing ingredients to a jam jar and shake really well for about a minute.
- Just before serving, add dressing or bring to the table with the dressing in a jug.

Sweet Treat

Raw Vanilla and Raspberry Cheesecake

This is a healthy food for any time of the day. I have been known to eat it for breakfast and it takes all my willpower to stop at one slice. Tell most people that you're serving up a gluten-free, dairy-free, sugar-free dessert and their face will give a look that says, *Sure, why would you bother?* But this dessert is fabulous and, once they get past the description, most people devour it. I make this when friends or family are coming over and, because it's so popular, I finally started getting smart and now I make two.

The nuts in the base can be replaced with almond or brazil nuts or you can substitute in some seeds. Just keep the ratio of nuts to dates at about 3:1. You can add berries to the top for colour and extra flavour. Raspberries, strawberries, blackberries, blueberries or blackcurrants all work well. Alternatively, you can leave it as a plain vanilla-lemon cake.

Making this cake is decidedly easier with the right equipment. For the base you're going to want a food processor (like a Magimix) and, for the top, a jug blender (like a Vitamix). Without them, it's too much hard work.

Makes 1 cake (12-16 slices)

Ingredients:

Base:
- 100 g pitted dates, chopped and soaked
- 150 g pecan nuts
- 150 g hazelnuts
- 2 tbsp melted coconut oil
- pinch of sea salt
- 1 tbsp almond butter

Top:
- zest and juice of 1 lemon
- 200 g cashew nuts, soaked
- 2 tbsp maple syrup
- 3 tbsp melted coconut oil

- ▫ 1 tsp vanilla extract
- ▫ 1 400 ml can full-fat coconut milk, chilled in the fridge or freezer before opening

To Decorate:

- ▫ a small punnet of fresh raspberries

Method:

- ▫ There is a little bit of advance work required as the dates and cashews require soaking in advance. The cake also needs a little time to set so be sure to make it a few hours before serving.
- ▫ Soak the dates overnight in water (or espresso coffee if you feel like an extra kick), drain and place in the food processor. Add the remaining base ingredients and blitz. It's ready when the mixture starts to come together. If you're just getting loose crumbs that aren't sticking, add a few extra dates, a little of the water that you drained off the dates or a little more melted coconut oil.
- ▫ Spoon the mixture into a springform tin (23 cm works well). A little trick to get the base evenly distributed without making a mess. Take a piece of greaseproof paper bigger than the tin and put it over the mixture. Now, make your hand into a fist and press the base firmly and evenly into the tin using your knuckles. The greaseproof paper stops the mixture from getting all over your hand. Place in the fridge or freezer while you make the topping.
- ▫ Soak the cashews in water for about two hours before starting. They will double in size. Drain and place in the jug blender along with the zest and juice of the lemon, the maple syrup, melted coconut oil and vanilla extract. (If you're adding berries to the top, add them now.) Blend until really, really smooth. This is where having a good blender helps as the high power will do this job really easily.

- Next, take the can of chilled coconut milk and open it. When you use full-fat coconut milk, the thicker cream and the lighter water will have separated. You are looking to scoop all the set coconut cream into the jug blender and none of the lighter coconut water. Give the blender one last whizz once the coconut cream has been added.
- Pour this mixture over the base and pop it back in the fridge for about two hours to set.
- Open the springform tin gently and the cake should release easily.
- Add the fresh berries on top before serving.

Recovery Food

Recovery Protein Drink

What I call an 'essential food'. When I get to the final weeks of pre-race training I take this after every long run. This helps replenish my glycogen stores and repairs my muscles quickly. I have an old drink shaker left behind at one of my parents' 80's parties. I intend to use it someday but I haven't managed yet. I prefer the Vitamix, mainly because I don't have the energy for a vigorous shake after a long run. Sometimes I make it thick and have to shovel it in with a spoon. However, after a lot of long runs I don't feel like eating so I make it as a liquid drink.

Serves 1

Ingredients:
- 50 g oats
- 25 g protein powder (I use Sunwarrior, sprouted & fermented chocolate flavour)
- 1 tbsp cacao powder
- 1 tbsp cacao nibs
- 1 tbsp sunflower seeds
- 1 heaped tbsp almond butter
- 1 tsp cinnamon powder
- 1 small banana
- 1 cup of rice/almond/oat milk (or water)

Method:
- Put in a blender and mix. Add liquid to find your preferred consistency.

Anti-Inflammatory Tonic

A must for the joints after a long run. One day I hobbled into my local health food store (The Hopsack) after a particularly taxing run. The owner, Finn, told me to go home and mix this drink. Great to keep inflammation in check, especially for older runners whose natural healing powers have begun to wane. It is potent stuff but doesn't taste great, so I add maple syrup.

Serves 1

Ingredients:

- ¼ cup of apple cider vinegar
- 1 tsp cayenne pepper
- 1 tsp cinnamon powder
- 1 tsp turmeric powder
- maple syrup to taste
- a few twists of freshly ground pepper
- ½ cup hot, not boiling, water

Method:

- Mix everything, bar the water, in a mug to a thick paste. Top up with hot water, mix well and drink.

RUNNING INJURIES

Ultra-running is an endurance sport. But pain is not something that you should have to endure. When we look at people running a marathon or maybe their first ultra, we see the same things recurring. Bodies that are overrun, undernourished and underprepared, both mentally and physically. To protect yourself from the usual overuse running injuries, I suggest you complete the *Mobility Test* and follow the accompanying *Stretching Programme* in Section Two.

In this section, we look at how we combat the injuries that we may run into. Many of the most common injuries show early warning signs and expecting to *run it off* is unlikely to resolve an overuse injury. Rest can help resolve many issues, but if there is an underlying cause, then you would be best to speak to a sports physiotherapist.

Runner's knee (patellofemoral pain syndrome) is a general term that refers to pain in the front of your knee or around your kneecap. It's a common overuse injury in sports that involve running. Weakness in your hips or the muscles around your knee can put you at a higher risk of developing runner's knee. Strengthening around the hips can help prevent it.

Causes other than a structural defect include:

- ▶ weak thigh muscles
- ▶ tight hamstrings
- ▶ tight Achilles tendons
- ▶ poor foot support
- ▶ walking or running with the feet rolling in while the thigh muscles

pull the kneecap outward
▶ excessive training or overuse

How is runner's knee treated?
▶ cold packs
▶ elevating the leg
▶ compression knee wrap
▶ medicines such as ibuprofen
▶ stretching exercises
▶ strengthening exercises
▶ arch support in shoes

Achilles tendonitis refers to inflammation of the tendon that connects your calf muscle to your heel. It may happen after increasing your mileage or the intensity of your running. It can also occur if you do not give yourself sufficient rest. If left untreated, Achilles tendonitis increases your risk of rupturing your Achilles tendon. If this tendon is torn, it usually requires surgery to repair it.

While it may not be possible to prevent Achilles tendinitis, you can take measures to reduce your risk:

▶ Increase your activity level gradually. If you're just beginning an exercise programme, start slowly and gradually increase the duration and intensity of the training. Stick to the 10% rule. Never increase by more than 10% week to week.

▶ If you are engaging in an activity that places excessive stress on your tendons, such as hill running, always warm up first. If you notice pain during a particular exercise, stop and rest.

▶ Choose your shoes carefully. The shoes you wear while exercising should provide adequate cushioning for your heel and should have a firm arch support to help reduce the tension in the Achilles tendon. Replace any worn-out shoes. If your shoes are in good condition but don't support your feet, try arch supports in both shoes.

▶ Stretch daily. Take the time to stretch your calf muscles and

Achilles tendon in the morning, before exercise and after exercise to maintain flexibility. This is especially important to avoid a recurrence of Achilles tendonitis.

▶ Strengthen your calf muscles. Strong calf muscles enable the calf and Achilles tendon to better handle the stresses they encounter with activity and exercise.

▶ Cross-train. Alternate high-impact activities, such as running, with low-impact activities, such as swimming and cycling.

Iliotibial band syndrome is caused by repetitive friction of the iliotibial band rubbing against your leg bone. It is felt as a sharp pain on the outer side of your leg, usually just above your knee, which may be tender to the touch, especially during running when the heel strikes the ground. Your iliotibial band, commonly referred to as your IT band, is a long piece of connective tissue that runs from your outer hip to your knee. This band of tissue helps stabilise your knee when you're walking or running. It's very common in runners due to tight IT bands, weakness in your gluteal muscles, abdominals or hips.

Prevention includes maintaining flexibility and strength of the lower back, hips, knees and leg muscles, all key to avoiding recurrence.

Iliotibial band syndrome is treated by:

▶ Basic measures include rest, ice, compression and elevation – RICE.

▶ Physical therapy may be helpful. Surgery is rarely an option but is sometimes suggested for patients who develop chronic inflammation and who fail to respond to other treatment options.

Shin Splints (medial tibial stress syndrome) refer to pain that occurs in the front or the inner parts of your lower legs, along your shinbone. Shin splints can happen when you increase your running volume too quickly, especially when running on hard surfaces. Shin splints aren't serious in most cases and go away with rest. However, if you continue to run during this time they can develop into stress fractures.

Many runners experience mild shin soreness at one time or another, which can usually be tolerated. If shin splints are a persistent problem, you shouldn't run through it. If you have persistent shin splints try the following:

▶ Ice the inflamed area for 15 minutes three times a day and take an anti-inflammatory.

▶ Make sure you ice the shin area immediately after running. To speed recovery, cut down or stop running altogether. Typical recovery time is two to four weeks.

▶ If the injury doesn't respond to self-treatment and rest, see a sports physio who will be able to tell you if it is anything more serious. They might recommend custom-made insoles to control overpronation, or an X-ray to ensure there are no stress fractures.

▶ While recovering from shin splints, try alternative, non-impact exercises such as swimming, using a cross-trainer, walking and cycling in a low gear without standing up on the pedals.

Hamstring strains are both common and painful. They strike athletes of all sorts including runners, skaters and football, soccer and basketball players. If your hamstrings are tight, weak or tired, they may be more prone to injury. Unlike sprinters, it's reasonably uncommon for ultra-runners to experience a sudden hamstring tear. For the most part, distance runners experience hamstring strains that come on slowly and are caused by repetitive small tears in the fibres and connective tissue of the hamstring muscle.

A hamstring isn't actually a single 'string' but a group of three muscles that run along the back of your thigh. They allow you to bend your leg at the knee. During a hamstring strain, one or more of these muscles gets overloaded. The muscles might even start to tear. You're likely to get a hamstring strain during activities that involve a lot of running and jumping or sudden stopping and starting. Strengthening your hamstrings is one way to protect against hamstring strain.

Common causes for hamstring strain:

▶ You don't warm up before exercising.

▶ The muscles in the front of your thigh (the quadriceps) are tight as they pull your pelvis forward and tighten the hamstrings.

▶ Weak glutes. Glutes and hamstrings work together, so if the glutes are weak, hamstrings can be overloaded and become strained.

Regular treatment for a hamstring strain:

▶ Rest the leg. Avoid putting weight on the leg as best you can. If the pain is severe, you may need crutches until it goes away.

▶ Ice your leg to reduce pain and swelling. Do it for 20–30 minutes every three to four hours for two to three days, or until the pain is gone.

▶ Compress your leg. Use an elastic bandage around the leg to keep down swelling.

▶ Elevate your leg on a pillow when you're sitting or lying down.

▶ Take anti-inflammatory painkillers like ibuprofen to help with pain and swelling.

▶ Practice stretching and strengthening exercises.

Plantar fasciitis is one of the most common foot injuries. It is caused by damage to the thick layer of tissue, called fascia, on the bottom of your foot. This layer of tissue acts as a spring when you're walking or running. A main cause can be increasing your mileage too soon. Muscle tightness or weaknesses in your calves also contribute to plantar fasciitis.

Regular treatments – these are methods that are reasonably straightforward, inexpensive and can be done at home:

▶ Wear comfortable shoes with some cushioning and arch support, and avoid hard shoes or anything barefoot.

▶ Ice your foot several times a day. If you run, ice immediately afterwards.

▶ Stretch your calves at least three times per day.

▶ Stretch your plantar fascia three times per day. Try to stretch first thing in the morning.

▶ Wear a night splint to stretch out your arch, Achilles and calf muscles.

▶ Roll out your plantar fascia with a golf ball, taking care not to press too hard on the injured area.

Stress fractures are tiny hairline cracks that form in bone due to repetitive stress or impact. For runners, stress fractures often occur at the top of the foot, or in the heel or lower leg. Symptoms of a stress fracture typically include swelling, bruising and tenderness in the area of the fracture. The cause is over-running on a hard surface or poor posture.

Treatments include:

▶ RICE – rest, ice, compress and elevate the area.
▶ Get an X-ray. Do not phone a friend who may tell you not to worry, it's only shin splints. (Yes, that friend was me and when I saw the X-rays I was mortified.)

Ankle sprains are caused by overstretching the ligaments between your leg and ankle. Sprains often happen when you land on the outer part of your foot and roll your ankle over. Most of the time, ankle sprains improve with rest and self-care.

Treatment:

▶ RICE – rest, ice, compress and elevate the area.

MINIMUM TRAINING PLAN (KILOMETRES)

Week	Mon	Tue	Wed*	Thu	Fri	Sat	Sun	Total	*Wed
1	5 + stretch	Cross-train	8	10	Rest	19	8	50	
2	5 + stretch	Cross-train	8	10	Rest	23	8	54	
3	5 + stretch	Cross-train	8	10	Rest	26	8	57	
4	5 + stretch	Cross-train	5	8	Rest	23	8	49	
5	5 + stretch	Cross-train	8	11	Rest	26	11	61	Hills
6	5 + stretch	Cross-train	8	11	Rest	29	11	64	Fartlek
7	5 + stretch	Cross-train	8	11	Rest	29	16	69	Hills
8	5 + stretch	Cross-train	8	10	Rest	23	11	57	Fartlek
9	5 + stretch	Cross-train	8	11	Rest	34	8	66	Hills
10	5 + stretch	Cross-train	8	11	Rest	23	19	66	Fartlek
11	5 + stretch	Cross-train	8	11	Rest	39	10	73	Hills
12	5 + stretch	Cross-train	8	10	Rest	29	8	60	Fartlek
13	5 + stretch	Cross-train	8	11	Rest	32	16	72	Hills
14	5 + stretch	Cross-train	8	5	Rest	43	Rest	61	Fartlek
15	5 + stretch	Cross-train	6	11	Rest	23	16	61	Hills
16	5 + stretch	Cross-train	8	11	Rest	40	16	80	Fartlek
17	5 + stretch	Cross-train	8	11	Rest	43	19	86	Hills
18	5 + stretch	Cross-train	8	11	Rest	23	16	63	Fartlek
19	5 + stretch	Cross-train	Rest	5	Rest	80	Rest	90	
20	5 + stretch	Cross-train	8	10	Rest	23	8	54	Hills
21	5 + stretch	Cross-train	Rest	11	Rest	39	23	78	
22	5 + stretch	Cross-train	11	8	Rest	29	Rest	53	
23	5 + stretch	Cross-train	Rest	11	Rest	16	8	40	
24	5 + stretch	Cross-train	6	Rest	3	161	-	175	

ADVANCED TRAINING PLAN (KILOMETRES)

Week	Mon	Tue	Wed*	Thu	Fri	Sat	Sun	Total	*Wed
1	8 + stretch	Cross-train	10	11	Rest	19	8	**56**	
2	8 + stretch	Cross-train	10	11	Rest	23	10	**62**	
3	8 + stretch	Cross-train	10	13	Rest	26	10	**67**	
4	8 + stretch	Cross-train	8	11	Rest	23	8	**58**	
5	8 + stretch	Cross-train	**10**	13	Rest	29	13	**73**	Hills
6	8 + stretch	Cross-train	**10**	13	Rest	29	19	**79**	Fartlek
7	8 + stretch	Cross-train	**13**	10	Rest	32	16	**79**	Hills
8	8 + stretch	Cross-train	**8**	11	Rest	23	10	**60**	Fartlek
9	8 + stretch	Cross-train	**10**	13	Rest	32	19	**82**	Hills
10	8 + stretch	Cross-train	**10**	16	Rest	26	23	**83**	Fartlek
11	8 + stretch	Cross-train	**10**	13	Rest	39	19	**89**	Hills
12	8 + stretch	Cross-train	**10**	13	Rest	26	16	**73**	Fartlek
13	8 + stretch	Cross-train	**10**	16	Rest	29	23	**86**	Hills
14	8 + stretch	Cross-train	**10**	6	Rest	50	Rest	**74**	Fartlek
15	8 + stretch	Cross-train	**10**	16	Rest	26	16	**76**	Hills
16	8 + stretch	Cross-train	**10**	16	Rest	40	24	**98**	Fartlek
17	8 + stretch	Cross-train	**10**	16	Rest	40	29	**103**	Hills
18	8 + stretch	Cross-train	**10**	19	Rest	26	16	**79**	Fartlek
19	8 + stretch	Cross-train	**10**	6	Rest	80	Rest	**104**	Hills
20	8 + stretch	Cross-train	**10**	16	Rest	48	32	**114**	Fartlek
21	8 + stretch	Cross-train	**10**	13	Rest	48	32	**111**	Hills
22	8 + stretch	Cross-train	10	16	Rest	24	24	**82**	
23	8 + stretch	Cross-train	10	13	Rest	16	8	**55**	
24	8 + stretch	Cross-train	6	Rest	3	161	-	**178**	

BLANK WEEKLY PEAK PERFORMANCE CHARTS

WEEKLY PEAK PERFORMANCE CHART

		M	T	W	T	F	S	S	TOTAL
Stretching	2 x 2 points								/4
Recovery Run	1 x 2 points								/2
Hill Run / Fartlek Run	1 x 5 points								/5
Regular Run	2 x 1 points								/2
Long Run	1 x 5 points								/5
Alternative Exercise	1 x 2 points								/2
Rest & Recovery	2 x 3 points								/6
Sleep	7 x 1 points								/7
Education	3 x 1 points								/3
Food Planning	1 x 2 points								/2
Food Shopping	1 x 2 points								/2
Food Preparation	7 x 1 points								/7
Eating	7 x 2 points								/14
IST & Maintaining Pre-Season	1 x 4 points								/4
Mental Resilience	7 x 1 points								/7
Visualisation	2 x 1 points								/2
Self-talk	1 x 5 points								/5
Hydration	7 x 1 points								/7
Discipline & Consistency	7 x 1 points								/7
Laughter	7 x 1 points								/7
TOTAL									/100

Success is not final, failure is not fatal - it is the courage to continue that counts.
Sir Winston Churchill, Former Prime Minister of the United Kingdom

WEEKLY PEAK PERFORMANCE CHART

		M	T	W	T	F	S	S	TOTAL
Stretching	2 x 2 points								/4
Recovery Run	1 x 2 points								/2
Hill Run / Fartlek Run	1 x 5 points								/5
Regular Run	2 x 1 points								/2
Long Run	1 x 5 points								/5
Alternative Exercise	1 x 2 points								/2
Rest & Recovery	2 x 3 points								/6
Sleep	7 x 1 points								/7
Education	3 x 1 points								/3
Food Planning	1 x 2 points								/2
Food Shopping	1 x 2 points								/2
Food Preparation	7 x 1 points								/7
Eating	7 x 2 points								/14
IST & Maintaining Pre-Season	1 x 4 points								/4
Mental Resilience	7 x 1 points								/7
Visualisation	2 x 1 points								/2
Self-talk	1 x 5 points								/5
Hydration	7 x 1 points								/7
Discipline & Consistency	7 x 1 points								/7
Laughter	7 x 1 points								/7

TOTAL /100

Success is not final, failure is not fatal - it is the courage to continue that counts.
Sir Winston Churchill, Former Prime Minister of the United Kingdom

WEEKLY PEAK PERFORMANCE CHART

		M	T	W	T	F	S	S	TOTAL
Stretching	2 x 2 points								/4
Recovery Run	1 x 2 points								/2
Hill Run / Fartlek Run	1 x 5 points								/5
Regular Run	2 x 1 points								/2
Long Run	1 x 5 points								/5
Alternative Exercise	1 x 2 points								/2
Rest & Recovery	2 x 3 points								/6
Sleep	7 x 1 points								/7
Education	3 x 1 points								/3
Food Planning	1 x 2 points								/2
Food Shopping	1 x 2 points								/2
Food Preparation	7 x 1 points								/7
Eating	7 x 2 points								/14
IST & Maintaining Pre-Season	1 x 4 points								/4
Mental Resilience	7 x 1 points								/7
Visualisation	2 x 1 points								/2
Self-talk	1 x 5 points								/5
Hydration	7 x 1 points								/7
Discipline & Consistency	7 x 1 points								/7
Laughter	7 x 1 points								/7

TOTAL /100

Success is not final, failure is not fatal - it is the courage to continue that counts.
Sir Winston Churchill, Former Prime Minister of the United Kingdom

WEEKLY PEAK PERFORMANCE CHART

	M	T	W	T	F	S	S	TOTAL
Stretching 2 x 2 points								/4
Recovery Run 1 x 2 points								/2
Hill Run / Fartlek Run 1 x 5 points								/5
Regular Run 2 x 1 points								/2
Long Run 1 x 5 points								/5
Alternative Exercise 1 x 2 points								/2
Rest & Recovery 2 x 3 points								/6
Sleep 7 x 1 points								/7
Education 3 x 1 points								/3
Food Planning 1 x 2 points								/2
Food Shopping 1 x 2 points								/2
Food Preparation 7 x 1 points								/7
Eating 7 x 2 points								/14
IST & Maintaining Pre-Season 1 x 4 points								/4
Mental Resilience 7 x 1 points								/7
Visualisation 2 x 1 points								/2
Self-talk 1 x 5 points								/5
Hydration 7 x 1 points								/7
Discipline & Consistency 7 x 1 points								/7
Laughter 7 x 1 points								/7

TOTAL /100

Success is not final, failure is not fatal - it is the courage to continue that counts.
Sir Winston Churchill, Former Prime Minister of the United Kingdom

WEEKLY PEAK PERFORMANCE CHART

		M	T	W	T	F	S	S	TOTAL
Stretching	2 x 2 points								/4
Recovery Run	1 x 2 points								/2
Hill Run / Fartlek Run	1 x 5 points								/5
Regular Run	2 x 1 points								/2
Long Run	1 x 5 points								/5
Alternative Exercise	1 x 2 points								/2
Rest & Recovery	2 x 3 points								/6
Sleep	7 x 1 points								/7
Education	3 x 1 points								/3
Food Planning	1 x 2 points								/2
Food Shopping	1 x 2 points								/2
Food Preparation	7 x 1 points								/7
Eating	7 x 2 points								/14
IST & Maintaining Pre-Season	1 x 4 points								/4
Mental Resilience	7 x 1 points								/7
Visualisation	2 x 1 points								/2
Self-talk	1 x 5 points								/5
Hydration	7 x 1 points								/7
Discipline & Consistency	7 x 1 points								/7
Laughter	7 x 1 points								/7

TOTAL /100

Success is not final, failure is not fatal - it is the courage to continue that counts.
Sir Winston Churchill, Former Prime Minister of the United Kingdom

WEEKLY PEAK
PERFORMANCE CHART

		M	T	W	T	F	S	S	TOTAL
Stretching	2 x 2 points								/4
Recovery Run	1 x 2 points								/2
Hill Run / Fartlek Run	1 x 5 points								/5
Regular Run	2 x 1 points								/2
Long Run	1 x 5 points								/5
Alternative Exercise	1 x 2 points								/2
Rest & Recovery	2 x 3 points								/6
Sleep	7 x 1 points								/7
Education	3 x 1 points								/3
Food Planning	1 x 2 points								/2
Food Shopping	1 x 2 points								/2
Food Preparation	7 x 1 points								/7
Eating	7 x 2 points								/14
IST & Maintaining Pre-Season	1 x 4 points								/4
Mental Resilience	7 x 1 points								/7
Visualisation	2 x 1 points								/2
Self-talk	1 x 5 points								/5
Hydration	7 x 1 points								/7
Discipline & Consistency	7 x 1 points								/7
Laughter	7 x 1 points								/7

TOTAL /100

Success is not final, failure is not fatal - it is the courage to continue that counts.
Sir Winston Churchill. Former Prime Minister of the United Kingdom

WEEKLY PEAK PERFORMANCE CHART

		M	T	W	T	F	S	S	TOTAL
Stretching	2 x 2 points								/4
Recovery Run	1 x 2 points								/2
Hill Run / Fartlek Run	1 x 5 points								/5
Regular Run	2 x 1 points								/2
Long Run	1 x 5 points								/5
Alternative Exercise	1 x 2 points								/2
Rest & Recovery	2 x 3 points								/6
Sleep	7 x 1 points								/7
Education	3 x 1 points								/3
Food Planning	1 x 2 points								/2
Food Shopping	1 x 2 points								/2
Food Preparation	7 x 1 points								/7
Eating	7 x 2 points								/14
IST & Maintaining Pre-Season	1 x 4 points								/4
Mental Resilience	7 x 1 points								/7
Visualisation	2 x 1 points								/2
Self-talk	1 x 5 points								/5
Hydration	7 x 1 points								/7
Discipline & Consistency	7 x 1 points								/7
Laughter	7 x 1 points								/7

TOTAL /100

Success is not final, failure is not fatal - it is the courage to continue that counts.
Sir Winston Churchill, Former Prime Minister of the United Kingdom

WEEKLY PEAK
PERFORMANCE CHART

	M	T	W	T	F	S	S	TOTAL
Stretching	2 x 2 points							/4
Recovery Run	1 x 2 points							/2
Hill Run / Fartlek Run	1 x 5 points							/5
Regular Run	2 x 1 points							/2
Long Run	1 x 5 points							/5
Alternative Exercise	1 x 2 points							/2
Rest & Recovery	2 x 3 points							/6
Sleep	7 x 1 points							/7
Education	3 x 1 points							/3
Food Planning	1 x 2 points							/2
Food Shopping	1 x 2 points							/2
Food Preparation	7 x 1 points							/7
Eating	7 x 2 points							/14
IST & Maintaining Pre-Season	1 x 4 points							/4
Mental Resilience	7 x 1 points							/7
Visualisation	2 x 1 points							/2
Self-talk	1 x 5 points							/5
Hydration	7 x 1 points							/7
Discipline & Consistency	7 x 1 points							/7
Laughter	7 x 1 points							/7

TOTAL /100

Success is not final, failure is not fatal - it is the courage to continue that counts.
Sir Winston Churchill, Former Prime Minister of the United Kingdom

WEEKLY PEAK PERFORMANCE CHART

		M	T	W	T	F	S	S	TOTAL
Stretching	2 x 2 points								/4
Recovery Run	1 x 2 points								/2
Hill Run / Fartlek Run	1 x 5 points								/5
Regular Run	2 x 1 points								/2
Long Run	1 x 5 points								/5
Alternative Exercise	1 x 2 points								/2
Rest & Recovery	2 x 3 points								/6
Sleep	7 x 1 points								/7
Education	3 x 1 points								/3
Food Planning	1 x 2 points								/2
Food Shopping	1 x 2 points								/2
Food Preparation	7 x 1 points								/7
Eating	7 x 2 points								/14
IST & Maintaining Pre-Season	1 x 4 points								/4
Mental Resilience	7 x 1 points								/7
Visualisation	2 x 1 points								/2
Self-talk	1 x 5 points								/5
Hydration	7 x 1 points								/7
Discipline & Consistency	7 x 1 points								/7
Laughter	7 x 1 points								/7

TOTAL /100

Success is not final, failure is not fatal - it is the courage to continue that counts.
Sir Winston Churchill, Former Prime Minister of the United Kingdom

WEEKLY PEAK PERFORMANCE CHART

		M	T	W	T	F	S	S	TOTAL
Stretching	2 x 2 points								/4
Recovery Run	1 x 2 points								/2
Hill Run / Fartlek Run	1 x 5 points								/5
Regular Run	2 x 1 points								/2
Long Run	1 x 5 points								/5
Alternative Exercise	1 x 2 points								/2
Rest & Recovery	2 x 3 points								/6
Sleep	7 x 1 points								/7
Education	3 x 1 points								/3
Food Planning	1 x 2 points								/2
Food Shopping	1 x 2 points								/2
Food Preparation	7 x 1 points								/7
Eating	7 x 2 points								/14
IST & Maintaining Pre-Season	1 x 4 points								/4
Mental Resilience	7 x 1 points								/7
Visualisation	2 x 1 points								/2
Self-talk	1 x 5 points								/5
Hydration	7 x 1 points								/7
Discipline & Consistency	7 x 1 points								/7
Laughter	7 x 1 points								/7

TOTAL /100

Success is not final, failure is not fatal - it is the courage to continue that counts.
Sir Winston Churchill, Former Prime Minister of the United Kingdom

WEEKLY PEAK
PERFORMANCE CHART

		M	T	W	T	F	S	S	TOTAL
Stretching	2 x 2 points								/4
Recovery Run	1 x 2 points								/2
Hill Run / Fartlek Run	1 x 5 points								/5
Regular Run	2 x 1 points								/2
Long Run	1 x 5 points								/5
Alternative Exercise	1 x 2 points								/2
Rest & Recovery	2 x 3 points								/6
Sleep	7 x 1 points								/7
Education	3 x 1 points								/3
Food Planning	1 x 2 points								/2
Food Shopping	1 x 2 points								/2
Food Preparation	7 x 1 points								/7
Eating	7 x 2 points								/14
IST & Maintaining Pre-Season	1 x 4 points								/4
Mental Resilience	7 x 1 points								/7
Visualisation	2 x 1 points								/2
Self-talk	1 x 5 points								/5
Hydration	7 x 1 points								/7
Discipline & Consistency	7 x 1 points								/7
Laughter	7 x 1 points								/7

TOTAL /100

Success is not final, failure is not fatal - it is the courage to continue that counts.
Sir Winston Churchill, Former Prime Minister of the United Kingdom

WEEKLY PEAK
PERFORMANCE CHART

	M	T	W	T	F	S	S	TOTAL
Stretching — 2 x 2 points								/4
Recovery Run — 1 x 2 points								/2
Hill Run / Fartlek Run — 1 x 5 points								/5
Regular Run — 2 x 1 points								/2
Long Run — 1 x 5 points								/5
Alternative Exercise — 1 x 2 points								/2
Rest & Recovery — 2 x 3 points								/6
Sleep — 7 x 1 points								/7
Education — 3 x 1 points								/3
Food Planning — 1 x 2 points								/2
Food Shopping — 1 x 2 points								/2
Food Preparation — 7 x 1 points								/7
Eating — 7 x 2 points								/14
IST & Maintaining Pre-Season — 1 x 4 points								/4
Mental Resilience — 7 x 1 points								/7
Visualisation — 2 x 1 points								/2
Self-talk — 1 x 5 points								/5
Hydration — 7 x 1 points								/7
Discipline & Consistency — 7 x 1 points								/7
Laughter — 7 x 1 points								/7

TOTAL /100

Success is not final, failure is not fatal - it is the courage to continue that counts.
Sir Winston Churchill, Former Prime Minister of the United Kingdom

224

WEEKLY PEAK PERFORMANCE CHART

		M	T	W	T	F	S	S	TOTAL
Stretching	2 x 2 points								/4
Recovery Run	1 x 2 points								/2
Hill Run / Fartlek Run	1 x 5 points								/5
Regular Run	2 x 1 points								/2
Long Run	1 x 5 points								/5
Alternative Exercise	1 x 2 points								/2
Rest & Recovery	2 x 3 points								/6
Sleep	7 x 1 points								/7
Education	3 x 1 points								/3
Food Planning	1 x 2 points								/2
Food Shopping	1 x 2 points								/2
Food Preparation	7 x 1 points								/7
Eating	7 x 2 points								/14
IST & Maintaining Pre-Season	1 x 4 points								/4
Mental Resilience	7 x 1 points								/7
Visualisation	2 x 1 points								/2
Self-talk	1 x 5 points								/5
Hydration	7 x 1 points								/7
Discipline & Consistency	7 x 1 points								/7
Laughter	7 x 1 points								/7

TOTAL /100

Success is not final, failure is not fatal - it is the courage to continue that counts.
Sir Winston Churchill, Former Prime Minister of the United Kingdom

WEEKLY PEAK PERFORMANCE CHART

		M	T	W	T	F	S	S	TOTAL
Stretching	2 x 2 points								/4
Recovery Run	1 x 2 points								/2
Hill Run / Fartlek Run	1 x 5 points								/5
Regular Run	2 x 1 points								/2
Long Run	1 x 5 points								/5
Alternative Exercise	1 x 2 points								/2
Rest & Recovery	2 x 3 points								/6
Sleep	7 x 1 points								/7
Education	3 x 1 points								/3
Food Planning	1 x 2 points								/2
Food Shopping	1 x 2 points								/2
Food Preparation	7 x 1 points								/7
Eating	7 x 2 points								/14
IST & Maintaining Pre-Season	1 x 4 points								/4
Mental Resilience	7 x 1 points								/7
Visualisation	2 x 1 points								/2
Self-talk	1 x 5 points								/5
Hydration	7 x 1 points								/7
Discipline & Consistency	7 x 1 points								/7
Laughter	7 x 1 points								/7

TOTAL /100

Success is not final, failure is not fatal - it is the courage to continue that counts.
Sir Winston Churchill, Former Prime Minister of the United Kingdom

WEEKLY PEAK PERFORMANCE CHART

		M	T	W	T	F	S	S	TOTAL
Stretching	2 x 2 points								/4
Recovery Run	1 x 2 points								/2
Hill Run / Fartlek Run	1 x 5 points								/5
Regular Run	2 x 1 points								/2
Long Run	1 x 5 points								/5
Alternative Exercise	1 x 2 points								/2
Rest & Recovery	2 x 3 points								/6
Sleep	7 x 1 points								/7
Education	3 x 1 points								/3
Food Planning	1 x 2 points								/2
Food Shopping	1 x 2 points								/2
Food Preparation	7 x 1 points								/7
Eating	7 x 2 points								/14
IST & Maintaining Pre-Season	1 x 4 points								/4
Mental Resilience	7 x 1 points								/7
Visualisation	2 x 1 points								/2
Self-talk	1 x 5 points								/5
Hydration	7 x 1 points								/7
Discipline & Consistency	7 x 1 points								/7
Laughter	7 x 1 points								/7

TOTAL /100

Success is not final, failure is not fatal - it is the courage to continue that counts.
Sir Winston Churchill, Former Prime Minister of the United Kingdom

WEEKLY PEAK
PERFORMANCE CHART

	M	T	W	T	F	S	S	TOTAL
Stretching	2 x 2 points							/4
Recovery Run	1 x 2 points							/2
Hill Run / Fartlek Run	1 x 5 points							/5
Regular Run	2 x 1 points							/2
Long Run	1 x 5 points							/5
Alternative Exercise	1 x 2 points							/2
Rest & Recovery	2 x 3 points							/6
Sleep	7 x 1 points							/7
Education	3 x 1 points							/3
Food Planning	1 x 2 points							/2
Food Shopping	1 x 2 points							/2
Food Preparation	7 x 1 points							/7
Eating	7 x 2 points							/14
IST & Maintaining Pre-Season	1 x 4 points							/4
Mental Resilience	7 x 1 points							/7
Visualisation	2 x 1 points							/2
Self-talk	1 x 5 points							/5
Hydration	7 x 1 points							/7
Discipline & Consistency	7 x 1 points							/7
Laughter	7 x 1 points							/7

TOTAL /100

Success is not final, failure is not fatal - it is the courage to continue that counts.
Sir Winston Churchill, Former Prime Minister of the United Kingdom

WEEKLY PEAK PERFORMANCE CHART

		M	T	W	T	F	S	S	TOTAL
Stretching	2 x 2 points								/4
Recovery Run	1 x 2 points								/2
Hill Run / Fartlek Run	1 x 5 points								/5
Regular Run	2 x 1 points								/2
Long Run	1 x 5 points								/5
Alternative Exercise	1 x 2 points								/2
Rest & Recovery	2 x 3 points								/6
Sleep	7 x 1 points								/7
Education	3 x 1 points								/3
Food Planning	1 x 2 points								/2
Food Shopping	1 x 2 points								/2
Food Preparation	7 x 1 points								/7
Eating	7 x 2 points								/14
IST & Maintaining Pre-Season	1 x 4 points								/4
Mental Resilience	7 x 1 points								/7
Visualisation	2 x 1 points								/2
Self-talk	1 x 5 points								/5
Hydration	7 x 1 points								/7
Discipline & Consistency	7 x 1 points								/7
Laughter	7 x 1 points								/7

TOTAL /100

Success is not final, failure is not fatal - it is the courage to continue that counts.
Sir Winston Churchill, Former Prime Minister of the United Kingdom

WEEKLY PEAK
PERFORMANCE CHART

		M	T	W	T	F	S	S	TOTAL
Stretching	2 x 2 points								/4
Recovery Run	1 x 2 points								/2
Hill Run / Fartlek Run	1 x 5 points								/5
Regular Run	2 x 1 points								/2
Long Run	1 x 5 points								/5
Alternative Exercise	1 x 2 points								/2
Rest & Recovery	2 x 3 points								/6
Sleep	7 x 1 points								/7
Education	3 x 1 points								/3
Food Planning	1 x 2 points								/2
Food Shopping	1 x 2 points								/2
Food Preparation	7 x 1 points								/7
Eating	7 x 2 points								/14
IST & Maintaining Pre-Season	1 x 4 points								/4
Mental Resilience	7 x 1 points								/7
Visualisation	2 x 1 points								/2
Self-talk	1 x 5 points								/5
Hydration	7 x 1 points								/7
Discipline & Consistency	7 x 1 points								/7
Laughter	7 x 1 points								/7

TOTAL /100

Success is not final, failure is not fatal - it is the courage to continue that counts.
Sir Winston Churchill, Former Prime Minister of the United Kingdom

WEEKLY PEAK
PERFORMANCE CHART

		M	T	W	T	F	S	S	TOTAL
Stretching	2 x 2 points								/4
Recovery Run	1 x 2 points								/2
Hill Run / Fartlek Run	1 x 5 points								/5
Regular Run	2 x 1 points								/2
Long Run	1 x 5 points								/5
Alternative Exercise	1 x 2 points								/2
Rest & Recovery	2 x 3 points								/6
Sleep	7 x 1 points								/7
Education	3 x 1 points								/3
Food Planning	1 x 2 points								/2
Food Shopping	1 x 2 points								/2
Food Preparation	7 x 1 points								/7
Eating	7 x 2 points								/14
IST & Maintaining Pre-Season	1 x 4 points								/4
Mental Resilience	7 x 1 points								/7
Visualisation	2 x 1 points								/2
Self-talk	1 x 5 points								/5
Hydration	7 x 1 points								/7
Discipline & Consistency	7 x 1 points								/7
Laughter	7 x 1 points								/7

TOTAL /100

Success is not final, failure is not fatal - it is the courage to continue that counts.
Sir Winston Churchill, Former Prime Minister of the United Kingdom

WEEKLY PEAK
PERFORMANCE CHART

		M	T	W	T	F	S	S	TOTAL
Stretching	2 x 2 points								/4
Recovery Run	1 x 2 points								/2
Hill Run / Fartlek Run	1 x 5 points								/5
Regular Run	2 x 1 points								/2
Long Run	1 x 5 points								/5
Alternative Exercise	1 x 2 points								/2
Rest & Recovery	2 x 3 points								/6
Sleep	7 x 1 points								/7
Education	3 x 1 points								/3
Food Planning	1 x 2 points								/2
Food Shopping	1 x 2 points								/2
Food Preparation	7 x 1 points								/7
Eating	7 x 2 points								/14
IST & Maintaining Pre-Season	1 x 4 points								/4
Mental Resilience	7 x 1 points								/7
Visualisation	2 x 1 points								/2
Self-talk	1 x 5 points								/5
Hydration	7 x 1 points								/7
Discipline & Consistency	7 x 1 points								/7
Laughter	7 x 1 points								/7

TOTAL /100

Success is not final, failure is not fatal - it is the courage to continue that counts.
Sir Winston Churchill, Former Prime Minister of the United Kingdom

WEEKLY PEAK PERFORMANCE CHART

		M	T	W	T	F	S	S	TOTAL
Stretching	2 x 2 points								/4
Recovery Run	1 x 2 points								/2
Hill Run / Fartlek Run	1 x 5 points								/5
Regular Run	2 x 1 points								/2
Long Run	1 x 5 points								/5
Alternative Exercise	1 x 2 points								/2
Rest & Recovery	2 x 3 points								/6
Sleep	7 x 1 points								/7
Education	3 x 1 points								/3
Food Planning	1 x 2 points								/2
Food Shopping	1 x 2 points								/2
Food Preparation	7 x 1 points								/7
Eating	7 x 2 points								/14
IST & Maintaining Pre-Season	1 x 4 points								/4
Mental Resilience	7 x 1 points								/7
Visualisation	2 x 1 points								/2
Self-talk	1 x 5 points								/5
Hydration	7 x 1 points								/7
Discipline & Consistency	7 x 1 points								/7
Laughter	7 x 1 points								/7
								TOTAL	/100

Success is not final, failure is not fatal - it is the courage to continue that counts.
Sir Winston Churchill, Former Prime Minister of the United Kingdom

WEEKLY PEAK PERFORMANCE CHART

		M	T	W	T	F	S	S	TOTAL
Stretching	2 x 2 points								/4
Recovery Run	1 x 2 points								/2
Hill Run / Fartlek Run	1 x 5 points								/5
Regular Run	2 x 1 points								/2
Long Run	1 x 5 points								/5
Alternative Exercise	1 x 2 points								/2
Rest & Recovery	2 x 3 points								/6
Sleep	7 x 1 points								/7
Education	3 x 1 points								/3
Food Planning	1 x 2 points								/2
Food Shopping	1 x 2 points								/2
Food Preparation	7 x 1 points								/7
Eating	7 x 2 points								/14
IST & Maintaining Pre-Season	1 x 4 points								/4
Mental Resilience	7 x 1 points								/7
Visualisation	2 x 1 points								/2
Self-talk	1 x 5 points								/5
Hydration	7 x 1 points								/7
Discipline & Consistency	7 x 1 points								/7
Laughter	7 x 1 points								/7

TOTAL /100

Success is not final, failure is not fatal - it is the courage to continue that counts.
Sir Winston Churchill, Former Prime Minister of the United Kingdom

WEEKLY PEAK PERFORMANCE CHART

		M	T	W	T	F	S	S	TOTAL
Stretching	2 x 2 points								/4
Recovery Run	1 x 2 points								/2
Hill Run / Fartlek Run	1 x 5 points								/5
Regular Run	2 x 1 points								/2
Long Run	1 x 5 points								/5
Alternative Exercise	1 x 2 points								/2
Rest & Recovery	2 x 3 points								/6
Sleep	7 x 1 points								/7
Education	3 x 1 points								/3
Food Planning	1 x 2 points								/2
Food Shopping	1 x 2 points								/2
Food Preparation	7 x 1 points								/7
Eating	7 x 2 points								/14
IST & Maintaining Pre-Season	1 x 4 points								/4
Mental Resilience	7 x 1 points								/7
Visualisation	2 x 1 points								/2
Self-talk	1 x 5 points								/5
Hydration	7 x 1 points								/7
Discipline & Consistency	7 x 1 points								/7
Laughter	7 x 1 points								/7

TOTAL /100

Success is not final, failure is not fatal - it is the courage to continue that counts.
Sir Winston Churchill, Former Prime Minister of the United Kingdom

WEEKLY PEAK PERFORMANCE CHART

		M	T	W	T	F	S	S	TOTAL
Stretching	2 x 2 points								/4
Recovery Run	1 x 2 points								/2
Hill Run / Fartlek Run	1 x 5 points								/5
Regular Run	2 x 1 points								/2
Long Run	1 x 5 points								/5
Alternative Exercise	1 x 2 points								/2
Rest & Recovery	2 x 3 points								/6
Sleep	7 x 1 points								/7
Education	3 x 1 points								/3
Food Planning	1 x 2 points								/2
Food Shopping	1 x 2 points								/2
Food Preparation	7 x 1 points								/7
Eating	7 x 2 points								/14
IST & Maintaining Pre-Season	1 x 4 points								/4
Mental Resilience	7 x 1 points								/7
Visualisation	2 x 1 points								/2
Self-talk	1 x 5 points								/5
Hydration	7 x 1 points								/7
Discipline & Consistency	7 x 1 points								/7
Laughter	7 x 1 points								/7

TOTAL /100

Success is not final, failure is not fatal - it is the courage to continue that counts.
Sir Winston Churchill. Former Prime Minister of the United Kingdom

EPILOGUE

I found loneliness in pain. It made me feel hollow and useless. When I came out the other side, after being stripped of all my safety nets, I somehow left with an appreciation and a hint of gratitude. Gratitude that the pain, once relentless, was gone. Gratitude that I could appreciate the small moments; a taste, a laugh, even the feeling of rain on my face.

I finished my third 100-miler, the Connemara 100, in 27 hours and 37 minutes. I have entered the race again this August. I have set myself the target of finishing in under 24 hours. By challenging myself this way I know it will help me to make better choices, every day. Focusing my energy on getting mentally and physically prepared for the challenge ahead. I contracted COVID-19 in January 2021. It set me back mentally and physically to the point where I was not sure that I would ever run an ultra again. Thankfully I have recovered and I want to enjoy the training, have fun in the whole process and the actual race. I don't want to waste this opportunity.

No doubt some readers will reach the end of this book and think, *But sure I'm doing more/different/better training than this. Why hasn't he mentioned X/Y/Z?* I don't for a second think I have it all figured out but I like to think that I have learned a lot since the first thought of running an ultramarathon crossed my mind. My learning and experience is what you find in these pages. I hope this book gives you the confidence to take on your first ultramarathon and the tools to make it something you will be forever proud of.

ABOUT THE AUTHOR

Jonathan has three children, Shay, Jem and Chris, and is stepfather to Sarah. He currently lives in West Cork in Ireland with his wife Fiona. It is rural and sparsely populated in winter. He runs most days on the Sheep's Head peninsula, often without meeting another person. To get a handle on the mental side of endurance running, he went to college in 2019 to study sport psychology. Before COVID-19 he liked to surround himself with runners whenever possible. Since he started running at age 45, he has completed 15 marathons and six ultras.

This is his second book. His first, *The Plant-Based Runner: A Personal Guide to Running, Healthy Eating, and Discovering a New You*, is about how an ordinary overweight person went from being unable to run a mile to running daily and feeling good about himself.

BEFORE YOU GO

When I started running in 2009, I never thought for a moment that I would write about my experience.

I wrote my first book *The Plant-Based Runner* when I realised that I couldn't have been the only middle-aged man that no longer recognised himself when he looked in the mirror. Writing that book was something I did early in the morning before I went to work. I spent a few years digging around inside myself for the words to tell my story. It was a personal project at that point and I wasn't even sure that it would ever be published. I shared sections with Fiona to read every now and again, and she told me that it was good. She laughed, and cried, at all the right places but I wasn't sure that she was the best judge so, once I had a completed draft, I asked others to read it. People that knew me, and some strangers.

When I finally published it I wondered if my mum and dad would be the only ones with enough of a reason to read it. I never dreamt that over two years later, *The Plant-Based Runner* would still spend its time in and out of the top 50 of Amazon's *Athletics Biographies, Running & Jogging, Extreme Sports, Gluten Free Diets* and *Divorce & Separation* categories in both the UK and US. The feeling I get when I see the cover sitting alongside some of my heroes is only beaten by the absolute joy when one of my readers takes the time to reach out to me.

I read every review I find, and reply to every Facebook, Instagram and email message I get. The fact that my book has given thousands of people some of the tools they needed to improve their health gives me endless pleasure. It's these people and their comments that made me think that there might be an audience for another book, for the stage I'm now at with my running.

This book took more work. I went back to college and studied sport psychology, ran thousands of miles, read everything I could get my hands on about running ultras and tried different ways of training and eating. Slowly, the concept for *From Marathon to Ultra* took shape and came to life. I hope it gives you some of what you need to build the confidence, courage and grit to take on your first ultra.

So that brings me to ask, would you leave a review of this book wherever you bought it? I would love to know if the things that helped me train for and run ultramarathons have gone on to help you. Your review will have a direct impact on the success of this book, helping me to reach new runners and readers.

Thanks and happy running,
Jonathan

You can follow me at:
www.jcruns.com
Instagram @jc_plant_based_runner
Facebook @ThePlantBasedRunner
Or email hello@jcruns.com

Printed in Great Britain
by Amazon

80839823R00148